Animal Sciences

Pasha A. Lyvers Peffer
Michael L. Day
The Ohio State University

Kendall Hunt
publishing company

Kendall Hunt
publishing company

www.kendallhunt.com
Send all inquiries to:
4050 Westmark Drive
Dubuque, IA 52004-1840

ISBN 978-0-7575-8901-0

Printed in the United States of America

10 9 8 7 6 5 4 3

Contents

Acknowledgements

We offer our thanks to Introductory Animal Sciences students Anna K. Collins and Christine M. Widmann for their contributions to the text, its content, and organization; and colleagues that provided content and assisted in editing. We also acknowledge the Price Chair Teaching Improvement Grants Program.

Importance of Animals

"Each species is a masterpiece, a creation assembled with extreme care and genius."

—*Edward O. Wilson*

This text concerns the use of animals and introduces basic principles and practices that allow humans to successfully coexist with animals in captive and controlled environments. The importance of animals is depicted throughout history and modern society through rich displays of human and animal interactions in engravings, sculptures, paintings, and drawings, some of which date to forty thousand years ago. Humans and animals sustain a relationship of mutual benefit. Although modern uses of animals differs throughout the world, humans have relied on animals as a source of food, clothing, knowledge, energy, power, transportation, companionship, entertainment, service, and capital. Animals in turn rely on humans to provide food, shelter, companionship, and protection.

The relationship between humans and animals has been cultivated by the domestication process. The domestication process is relatively new in human history, occurring as recently as fourteen thousand years ago according to some estimates. The rise of human civilization is attributed to the ability to domesticate animals, which results in animals becoming adapted to humans and a captive environment. Although the origins of domestication are disputed, the process coincided with the development of agrarian societies. As the human population began to increase there was development of community living near water resources. The number of animals available for hunting began to decrease in these regions and a more stable source of food was required. Domestication provided a readily available source of food. Archeological evidence traces the earliest origins of domestication to Mesopotamia, the cradle of civilization occupied by

modern day Iran and Iraq. Findings suggest that domestication attempts were not always successful. Certain innate traits including social dominance and adaptability have contributed to the success of domestication and while the primary reasons for domestication were a stable food supply, the uses of animals have co-evolved with human needs.

Animals as a source of food continue to represent a primary use in modern society. It is generally accepted that humans are omnivorous, relying on both plant and animal products for optimal nutrition. The United States food pyramid, which provides guidance to a healthy diet, includes choices for low-fat or lean meat and poultry as well as milk, yogurt, and cheese. The inclusion of animal products in the diet is practiced by the majority of the population. The total calories derived from animal products in the United States are 26%, whereas animal products contribute to 69% of total protein consumed. Recent surveys place less than 1% of the United States population as practicing vegans, whom exclude the use of all animal products, and less than 3% as vegetarians, whom exclude the consumption of meat, poultry, and seafood. For the vegetarian diet, dairy remains an important component for many. While cow's milk is primarily consumed in the United States, water buffalo, goat, sheep, camel, yak, mare, sow, reindeer, and llama milk have been consumed throughout the world.

The importance of animals extends beyond their use as food. Conservation agriculture, which promotes sustainable use of land, relies on animals for land management. The grazing habits of animals are used throughout the world for erosion control, range or pasture management including plant diversification, and noxious weed control. Grazing animals can subsist on land that cannot be cultivated and in turn provide products such as meat and milk that can be used. Although animal use in transportation

Time Line of Domestication

Years Before Present	Species
12,000	
10,000	
9,000	
6,000	
5,000	
4,000	
3,000	
2,000	
1,000	
0	

■ **Fig. 1.1** The origins of domestication remain uncertain. It is generally accepted that the wolf was the first species domesticated, followed by goats and sheep. It is unknown if domestication of the wolf was driven by man, or wolf. Some suggest that wolves drove their own domestication. Scavenging from human refuse, wolves less likely to flee thrived in this environment and were more likely to undergo the changes associated with the domestication process. Research mice, and some fish, have been considered the most recent of animals to experience domestication. (Animal images © Nebojsa I, 2009. Under license from Shutterstock, Inc.)

has declined within the United States, animals remain vital to the transportation needs of other countries. In India, it is estimated that animal drawn carts have an economic value of five billion dollars and the cost to replace with more modern means of public transportation is estimated at $6 billion. In Sub-Saharan Africa the number of donkey drawn carts was estimated at one thousand in the 1960s and has grown to seventy-five thousand in recent years. By-products from the animal industries may one day reduce the dependence of the world on oil. In attempts to expand the petroleum base, research has been conducted to refine chicken fat for use as a biodiesel. Research in the animal industries also has been integral toward the discoveries into how biological systems function for the advancement of all animals, including humans. Since the end of the nineteenth century animals have contributed to over 50% of total scientific discoveries and 2/3 of the Noble Prizes awarded have been for discoveries involving animals. Although rats and mice have been the predominant animals used in some research

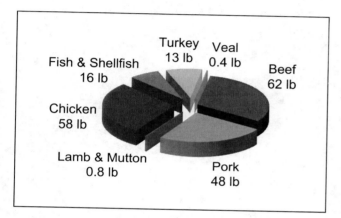 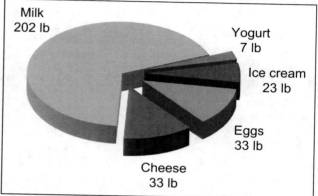

■ **Fig. 1.2**   Per capita consumption estimates of meat (left) and dairy, and eggs (right.) Choices of animal products for consumption are influenced by income, age, health consciousness, ethnicity, as well as value-added availability and risk perceptions.

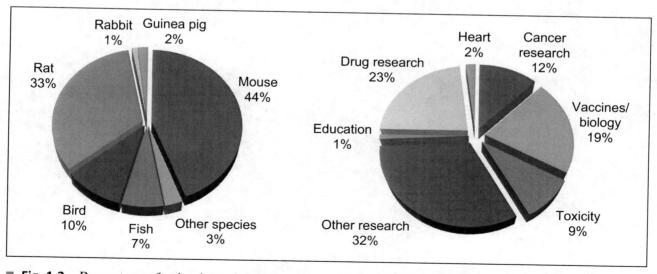

■ **Fig. 1.3**   Percentage of animal species commonly used in research (left). Food animals are represented by the category "Other species." Animals greatly contribute to research in fundamental biology and pharmaceutical development. The use of animals in education is relatively minor (right).

areas and especially in biomedical research, food animals have been integral in increasing knowledge concerning essential nutrient requirements, therapies for cancer, mechanisms of diabetes, surgical techniques, and mechanisms of immunity. The use of food animals in biomedical research is expanding. The anatomical and physiological similarities between pigs and humans have promoted the use of the former in determining the role of genetics, nutrition, and exercise in obesity and related complications, including heart disease. Sheep are providing insight into the role of maternal environment on fetal development and disease later in life and chickens may hold the key to understanding ovarian cancer in women. While the use of food animals in biomedical research has expanded, food animals remain crucial to the continued improvements in efficiency of production, product quantity and quality, and healthfulness of food obtained from these animals.

To continue to foster the human-animal relationship, knowledge of the principles of behavior, nutrition, genetics, reproduction and production of the various food animal species as influenced by environment and interactions with humans must be disseminated to each generation. Understanding of the relevance of these biological disciplines to producing healthy, well managed animals in harmony with environmental and social concerns.

Animal Behavior

"Behavior is too important to be left to psychologists."

—Donald Griffin (1915-2003)

This chapter introduces the basic principles of animal behavior and the approaches to defining and studying animal behavior for establishing acceptable animal practices that promote animal well being. The role of genetics and the environment on behaviors is highlighted. You will gain an understanding of the various behaviors that animal species employ, how behaviors develop, and how animals learn. Some common abnormal behaviors and behavioral disorders, and factors that contribute to their development, are presented.

Behavior: A Historical Perspective

Even before the process of domestication, the behavior of animals was of interest to humans. The earliest observations of animal behavior are depicted in human artifacts and a basic understanding of behavior was important in man's attempts to domesticate animals. The study of animal behavior as a science began with Aristotle around 300 B.C. In his works, Aristotle recorded his observations and ideas of animal behavior. In 1676, naturalist John Ray theorized that complex behaviors are innate and develop without learning. Another famous naturalist, Charles Darwin, wrote "The Expression of the Emotions in Man and Animals" in 1872. This seminal work depicted how animals and humans express and relate their emotions to others. Despite these early attempts to define behavior, the importance of behavior as a field of scientific study would not be realized until the late twentieth century. In 1962 Hafez completed the first text on the behaviors of domesticated animals, and in 1967

Fox proposed the teaching of behavior in agriculture and veterinary practice. However, the behavior of agricultural species did not receive full attention until the mid 1990's, coincident with the development of large, intensive systems of concentrated livestock production. In 1997, the USDA opened the livestock Behavior Research Unit at Purdue University with the mission:

> *to determine behavioral and physiological indicators of stress and/or well-being in food-producing animals and to develop management systems that maximize well-being in farm animals*

This center aims to understand the biological basis of animal behavior through promoting collaborations among ethologists, physiologists, immunologists and others.

■ **Fig. 2.1** The scratching by the hind limb placed over the forelimb is an innate behavior that many birds and mammals display. This form of complex behavior occurs without learning. Many innate behaviors are considered instinctive. (© Cheryl ann Quigley, 2009. Under license from Shutterstock, Inc.)

Introduction to the Study of Behavior

The psychology of animals has been studied since the early 1900's; however, the original application was toward man and not the animal under study. The recognition of the importance of the study of animal behavior for the animal has led to the establishment of four major approaches to the study of behavior:

1. Comparative psychology—the study of the mechanisms controlling behavior including: learning, sensation, perception, and genetics. This approach has been accepted and used for many years by psychologists, physiologists, and cognitive scientists.
2. Sociobiology—the study of the biological basis of social behavior. An emphasis is placed on the role of genetics in controlling expressed behaviors. Sociobiology considers the evolutionary advantage of inheriting behaviors.
3. Behavioral ecology—the study of the relationship between a behavior and its environment is behavioral ecology.
4. Ethology—the study of animals' behavior in their natural surroundings with a focus on instinctive or innate behaviors. Ethology is the scientific study of animal behavior in the animal's natural habitat.

■ **Fig. 2.2** The relationship between behaviors and the environment is a concern of animal scientists. Domesticated pigs raised in indoor confinement operations often display the bar biting behavior. The basis of this behavior is not fully understood, but it is suggested to be a manifestation of the rooting reflex exhibited by feral and wild pigs. (© Shawn Hine, 2009. Under license from Shutterstock, Inc.)

The field of ethology was once limited to the study of wild animals, but it has expanded to include domestic species in their usual surroundings and is referred to as applied ethology. Scientists studying ethology have developed ethograms, which are catalogs of the range of behaviors an animal exhibits in its environment. Ethograms aim to account for environmental circumstances that impact an animal's behavior that may be reflected by their domestication and/or captivity. Konrad Lorenz (1903-1989) is accredited as the founder of ethology and his discovery of imprinting, the learning process that occurs quite rapidly within a few hours or days following hatch in birds and birth in mammals, is an important aspect of ethology. Imprinting is a relatively irreversible process and results in offspring recognition of its mother and its species.

The Influence of Domestication and Genetics on Behavior

During the process of domestication, animals were inadvertently selected for traits that allowed for their control and management. There are several behavioral traits found in most domestic animals that promote their success in a captive environment and may have allowed for successful domestication. These behaviors include: gregariousness, social organization, promiscuous matings, precocial young, adaptability, limited agility, and docile temperament.

Agricultural animal species are generally docile, with attenuation of aggressive behavior considered a consequence of the domestication process. In addition, they are gregarious and are most content in organized groups that are established through social dominance. These animals traditionally do not rely on pair-bonding for mating as some wild species do, including beavers, golden eagles, swans, and wolves. If this were the case, it would be necessary to have one bull for every cow or one boar for every sow, which would not allow for efficient production systems. The offspring are precocial, well developed at birth and do not require extensive maternal care. Hoofed animals including foals, calves, pigs, lambs, and kids are born with their eyes open and are ambulatory shortly after birth. Adaptability to various environments, which includes management systems and diets, also has contributed to the success of these domestic animals.

Many of the behaviors that promoted successful domestication are considered instinctive behaviors. Instinctive, or innate, behaviors are those that an animal will exhibit without having any opportunity to learn. Examples of these behaviors include: suckling, pecking, and nest building. These behavioral characteristics may be inherited and can be altered by selection. Laying hens in production systems may display what is characterized as non-aggressive feather pecking directed toward the plumage of other birds. Considered a manifestation of the exploratory behaviors used to seek food, the behavior results in the deterioration of the plumage. When birds that display a reduction in this behavior are selected for breeding, the incidence of feather pecking decreases over subsequent generations, implicating the role of genetics in generational changes of this behavior. In wild populations natural selection is the primary stimulus altering inheritance of behaviors. Natural selection also played a role in inherited behaviors during domestication. Animals that adapted to confinement remained healthy and reproduced, while animals that did not adapt did not reproduce, or were at least less efficient. Consequently, a higher proportion of animals in each successive generation were more adapted to a human controlled environment. Today, artificial selection plays a greater role in inherited behaviors for captive animals.

The Role of Environment on Behavior

While the genetics of an animal are established at conception, the environment will influence the animal's behavior its entire life. Environmental effects on behavior begin during fetal development. Studies in rodents and monkeys have demonstrated that psychological stress on the mother during gestation, particularly during periods of rapid fetal development of the brain and nervous tissue, can program abnormal behavior in the offspring.

During postnatal development, environmental influences on behavior may include learning processes such as imprinting, animal management practices, and photoperiod. Learning is the modification of behaviors in response to specific experiences. Learned responses may range from associative learning, where an animal associates one stimulus to another, to the more controversial higher-order problem solving abilities. With regards to management practices, when animals are managed as groups an animal's behavior may be affected by the size of its herd or flock, as well as the age, sex, and dominance ranks of the other members of the group. For example, animals will tend to reach puberty earlier when kept with their own species, particularly if they are kept near members of the opposite sex. Photoperiod influences reproductive behavior and establishes the breeding seasons of sheep, goats, and horses; and increases egg laying capacity in chickens. Natural photoperiods can be manipulated and reproductive behaviors can be induced through artificial photoperiods. For example, increasing day length will generally stimulate egg production while decreasing the day length will suppress it.

■ **Fig. 2.3**   Nest building behaviors are common in many species prior to hatch or birth, including pigs, and are considered instinctive. (© Four Oaks, 2009. Under license from Shutterstock, Inc.)

Physiological Aspects of Behavior

Animals are able to perceive their environment through sensory receptors of the nervous system which receives visual, auditory, tactile, and olfactory information. The body can initiate a response to such stimuli through: 1) the spinal cord, 2) the hypothalamus, and 3) the cerebral cortex. Reflex reactions are initiated at the spinal cord and are involuntary responses to stimuli. The hypothalamus is responsible for hunger and thirst sensations and emotions. The cerebral cortex plays a key role in memory and learning and has been associated with adverse behavioral changes in dogs.

Auditory

The hearing range of livestock and poultry is within the frequency range of humans, while dogs have the ability to perceive sounds at a much greater fre-

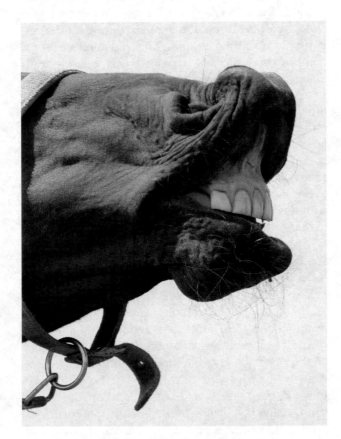

■ **Fig. 2.4** Horses will display the flehmen response to receive olfactory signals indicative of estrus in the female. (© Marcel Mooij, 2009. Under license from Shutterstock, Inc.)

quency. Livestock, and many other animals, have relatively large ears that can be directed independently. The ability of animals to move their ears allows them to detect and locate the source of a sound. The fact that they can move their ears independently also allows them to simultaneously hear sounds from opposite directions.

Olfactory

Many animals have a more acute sense of smell than humans as a consequence of an accessory olfactory organ known as the vomeronasal organ or Jacobson's organ. This organ is considered responsible for pheromone perception in animals and has been documented to influence exploratory behavior in rodents. Located between the mouth and the nasal cavities, it enables the animal to distinguish among odors that humans are unable to detect. When a bull, ram, or stallion smells the urine of a female to determine if she is in estrus, he is inspiring the scent of the urine into the vomeronasal organ for identification. As the male is inhaling, he will curl his upper lip. This action of lip-curling is called the flehmen response.

Tactile

Animals are acutely aware of their bodies and have a well-developed tactile sense. *Bos indicus* cattle have well developed subcutaneous muscle and are able to easily detect insects on their skin and dislodge them by selectively shaking these areas. Touch is an important aspect of communication as well. Animals will groom, lick, and scratch each other; and horses will often stand beside one another, head to tail, mutually swatting flies. Grooming in baboons is a behavioral pattern suggested to reduce tensions within the group. Observations suggest that pigs prefer to be close and physically against each other for tactile comfort.

Taste

Most animals readily distinguish between the four tastes: bitter, sweet, sour, and salty. Also, they can distinguish among the intensities of these flavors and their combinations. An exception is poultry. Poultry are considered to have a rather poor sense of taste and instead, rely primarily on sight. It has been demonstrated that feed intake can be increased in poultry by coloring the feed red or blue. In comparison flavor and odor have a greater influence on feed intake by cattle and horses.

Visual

A major distinction between different species is the size of their visual field. Eye placement on the side of the head provides grazing animals with an almost 360° field of vision. Grazing animals also have monocular vision. The wide field of monocular vision that grazing animals have allows them to watch a maximum area around them for potential predators. In contrast, predator species, including humans and birds of prey, have a larger field of binocular vision due to the frontal placement of their eyes. Binocular vision provides the animal with better depth perception, which allows predators to focus in on their prey. With monocular vision, blind spots are established directly in front and behind the animal. In the horse, these blind spots are equivalent to a loss of visual field four feet in front of the animal and ten feet directly behind the animal.

Communication

Auditory, olfactory, tactile and visual input also are important aspects of animal communication, along with vocalization. Animals can communicate in a variety of ways and understanding how they communicate is important for proper animal management, as well as for the safety of both the handler and the animal. Most communication between animals is within their own species, but some communication does occur across species. The vocalizations of animals have distinct meanings. For example, four to seven distinct vocalizations have been identified in the horse. A snort generally means danger or fear, while a whinny or nicker may signify distress. Chickens also have a feeding call that serves to attract other chickens to the feed. Mothers of all species will often call to their young and vice versa. When vocally communicating with an animal low, soft tones of longer duration are suggested to have a comforting or calming effect. Short, high-pitched tones are generally excitatory. Animals also rely on visual cues and body language to communicate. Postural changes in addition to eye contact and movement of the ears or tail confer meaning.

Fields of Behavioral Study

Studies of animal behavior may be conducted on wild, feral, captive, or domesticated animals. Through the study of behavior the significance and function of a behavior can be examined. Studies should provide for objective or straight forward assessment of an animal's behavior that can be analyzed without the confounding and often anthropomorphic interpretations of the observer. A fundamental question in the fields of behavioral study is: what are acceptable behaviors for a given animal under the conditions in which it is maintained? Because processes, including domestication,

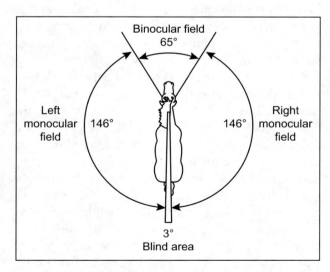

■ **Fig. 2.5**   The monocular vision of grazing animals provides a nearly 360° field of vision.

■ **Fig. 2.6**   Horses are expressive and convey varying degrees of excitement, playfulness, submission, or aggression using movement. (© Winthrop Brookhouse, 2009. Under license from Shutterstock, Inc.)

are required in the animal's diet as the body is incapable of producing adequate amounts of these nutrients to support the metabolic processes required for life. In contrast, nonessential, or dispensable, nutrients are not required in the diet.

Water

Water is the most overlooked nutrient despite the fact it is essential to all living things. Water constitutes 50-75% of an adult animal's body mass, up to 90% of a newborn animal's mass, 90% of blood in mammals, and 60-65% of the mass of a cell. Interestingly, the percent of Earth covered by water is 70% and falls neatly within these ranges as well.

Water serves two primary functions for all terrestrial animals: 1) a component in cellular metabolism, as biochemical reactions that occur in an animal's body require water; and 2) a medium for thermoregulation, the process of maintaining a constant body temperature independent of environmental factors.

Water is involved in many of the chemical reactions that take place in the body and is considered the universal solvent. Thus, it is important that water be present for many biological functions, since most compounds readily ionize or dissolve in water. An organism may obtain water through consumption or generate metabolic water within the body as a result of metabolism. Metabolic water is a substrate in hydrolysis, and a product in oxidation. Water is also a transport medium and a dilutent, and is required for the transportation of semisolid digesta in the gastrointestinal tract; as well as transportation of solutes in blood, tissues, cells, and exogenous secretions, such as urine and sweat.

Sources of water available to animals include potable water and feeds. Contribution of water to an animal through feeds is dependent on the type of feed and plant maturity. For example, most grains are approximately 10% water, while pasture grasses may exceed 80% water content. In addition, the water content of forages varies with plant maturity, with more mature forages containing less water. Water is lost from the animal through urination, defecation, and vaporization (sweat and respiration). Water lost through vaporization is important to thermoregulation. To maintain a constant body temperature, an animal must either generate heat if the environment is cooler than its body or have a way to dissipate heat if the environment is warmer

than its body. Animals dissipate heat through sweating or panting. The process of sweating is triggered by elevated body temperatures and activates sweat glands located beneath the skin. These activated glands produce water that is evaporated away from the body. The process of evaporation requires energy as water changes state during evaporation, this energy is received in the form of excess body heat. As sweat leaves the body and evaporates in the surrounding air it cools the skin. Animals with a limited number of sweat glands accomplish similar temperature regulation by panting. In this process, water is evaporated not from the skin, but from the oral cavity to maintain a standard body temperature.

Carbohydrates

Carbohydrates serve primarily as a source of energy for cellular processes, providing 4 kcal/g. They are the primary constituents of plant tissues and comprise approximately 70% or more of the dry matter of forages. Carbohydrates are classified as simple or complex. Sugars, which are monosaccharide and disaccharides, are simple carbohydrates, whereas complex carbohydrates include the polysaccharides starch and fiber.

■ **Fig. 3.1.3** Some animals are unable to sweat efficiently to cool the body. When excess heat needs to be dissipated in elephants, blood vessels dilate and increased blood flow through the capillaries of the ears occurs. Elephants may then flap their ears to effectively transfer heat into the environment. (© Four Oaks, 2009. Under license from Shutterstock, Inc.)

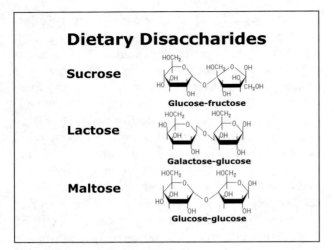

Fig. 3.1.4   Disaccharides

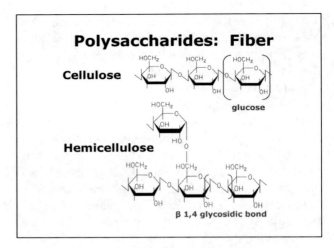

Fig. 3.1.6   Fiber

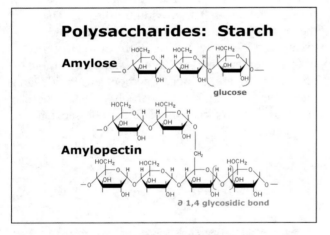

Fig. 3.1.5   Starch

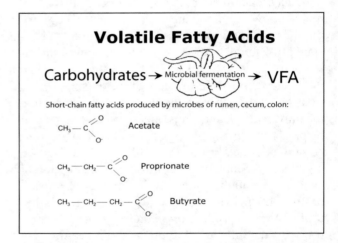

Fig. 3.1.7   Volatile fatty acids are byproducts from the microbial digestion of carbohydrates.

Sugars classified as monosaccharides include glucose, galactose and fructose. Glucose is the most important carbohydrate in biology and is used as a primary source of energy by most cell types. Following meal consumption, glucose not catabolized for energy may be stored as glycogen in liver and skeletal muscle tissues. Liver glycogen will be mobilized to maintain blood glucose and supply glucose to peripheral tissues in between meals. Skeletal muscle glycogen also will be mobilized in between meals; however, glucose that is released is only available to skeletal muscle tissue. Glucose also is a component of the disaccharides maltose, sucrose, and lactose. Maltose is derived from the glycosidic linkage of two glucose units, sucrose from the glycosidic linkage of glucose and fructose, and lactose from the glycosidic linkage of glucose and galactose. Lactose is more commonly referenced as milk sugar. Lastly, glucose serves as a precursor for the synthesis of proteins as well as lipids.

Starch includes polysaccharides such as amylose and amylopectin, which are formed from glucose molecules; however, amylose is a straight chain of glucose molecules, and amylopectin is branched. The branched organization of amylopectin results in a compact storage form of glucose for plants. The cereal grains (corn, barley, wheat, oats) are rich sources of starch, which is a readily digestible carbohydrate.

Classification of Lipids

Lipid Class	Functions
Fatty acids	metabolic fuel, metabolic intermediate, membrane anchors
Acylglycerols	fatty acid storage and transport
Phospholipids	membrane structure, storage of arachidonate
Sphingolipids	membrane structure, surface antigen, signal transduction
Ketone bodies	metabolic fuels
Polyisoprenes	cofactors and vitamins
Sterols	membrane structure, detergents, vitamins, hormones

Lipids are a diverse group of molecules that are related by their solubility in non-polar solvents. Lipids can be grouped into classes according to structural similarities, but the various classes do not share any characteristic chemical structural similarity.

Fiber is another form of complex carbohydrates and includes cellulose, hemicellulose, pectin, and lignin. These molecules are a main component of plants' cell walls and provide structural support to bolster the plant. Cellulose consists of only glucose units, whereas hemicelluloses, pectin, and lignin contain additional sugars. Dietary fibers are considered nondigestible carbohydrates as they are resistant to digestive enzymes of animal origin. However, microorganisms present in the forestomach of ruminants and hind-gut of nonruminants can break down dietary fiber through fermentation. This breakdown results in the production of the volatile fatty acids (VFA's) butyrate, acetate, and propionate. Butyrate and acetate are major energy sources, whereas propionate may be used as a precursor in the production of endogenous glucose. Because the body is capable of producing glucose from several precursor molecules, carbohydrates are not regarded as dietary essentials.

Lipids

Lipids are a group of organic compounds that are relatively insoluble in water, but are soluble in organic solvents. Fats and oils constitute the largest percent of lipids in most feedstuffs. Lipids are a more concentrated source of energy than carbohydrates or proteins, providing 9 kcal/g. Along with providing energy, lipids are a source of essential fatty acids, are an integral component of cell membranes, and serve as carriers of the fat-soluble vitamins, A, D, E, and K.

Approximately 95% of dietary lipid is supplied in the form of triglycerides. Triglycerides are compounds that have three fatty acids attached to a glycerol backbone. The hydrolysis, or breakdown, of triglycerides yields three fatty acids to one glycerol molecule. While fatty acids are a concentrated source of energy and may be stored as triglycerides in adipose tissue, glycerol is used as a precursor to glucose production. Most tissues can obtain the energy needed from the oxidation of glucose; however, in between meals or during a fast, fatty acids will be mobilized from adipose stores as some tissues switch from using glucose to fatty acid utilization.

Fatty acids consist of hydrocarbon chains ranging from two to 24 or more carbon atoms in length with a carboxyl group (-COOH) at the end of each chain. Most of the fatty acids found in animal tissues are straight chained (not branched) and contain an even number of carbons. When the carbons are connected only by single bonds and no double bonds exist, the fatty acid is saturated. The term saturated indicates that the fatty acids have the maximum number of hydrogen bonds, a property that causes saturated fats to be solid at room tempera-

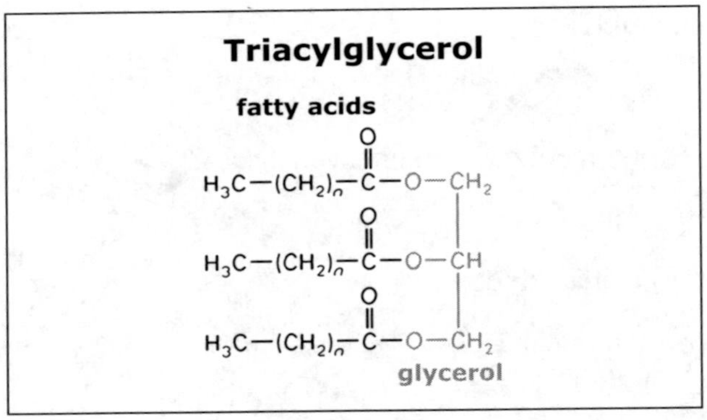

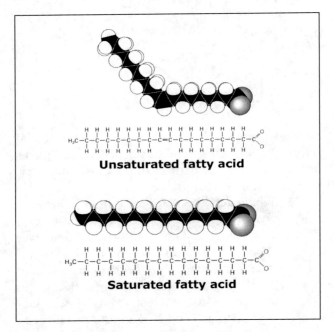

Triacylglycerol

fatty acids

Fig. 3.1.8 Structure of a triacylglycerol, commonly referred to as a triglyceride.

Unsaturated fatty acid

Saturated fatty acid

Fig. 3.1.9 Saturated versus unsaturated fatty acids.

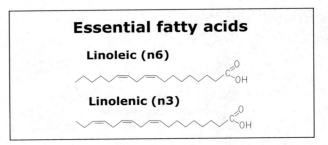

Cis **Trans**

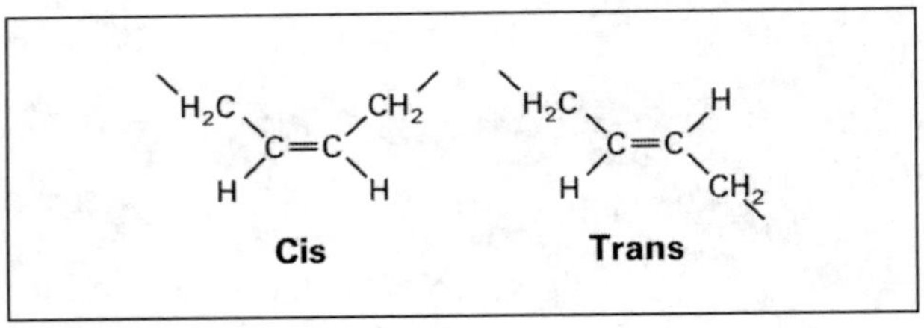

Fig. 3.1.10 Cis and trans isomers.

Essential fatty acids

Linoleic (n6)

Linolenic (n3)

Fig. 3.1.11 Essential fatty acids.

ture, indicating an increased melting point. In contrast, unsaturated fatty acids have one (monounsaturated) or more (polyunsaturated) double bonds. In unsaturated fatty acids, the chain of carbons does not contain the maximum number of hydrogens possible, resulting in a molecule that is less structured. Consequently, unsaturated fatty acids are liquid at room temperature. Unsaturated fats can occur as *cis* or *trans* isomers and refers to the orientation of hydrogens about the double bond. *Cis* indicates a structure in which the hydrogens adjacent to the double bond are oriented in the same direction (plane) and is the predominant isomer found in nature. *Trans* is a structure in which the hydrogens adjacent to the double bond are oriented in opposite direction (plane). Many dietary *trans* fats are produced commercially through hydrogenation, a chemical process in which hydrogens are added to unsaturated fats. An exception to this is the naturally occurring *trans* structure of the conjugated linoleic acid (CLA), which is produced by the microorganisms of the rumen. There are many reported health benefits of CLA's as they are considered to be a cancer fighting agent and have a role in reducing body fat. Because humans are incapable of producing CLA's, they must be obtained by consuming foods resulting from ruminants, such as milk, butter, beef, and lamb.

Two of the most important unsaturated fatty acids for animals are -linolenic acid (omega-3) and linoleic acid (omega-6). These fatty acids are recognized as dietary essentials and are precursors for the synthesis of longer chain polyunsaturated fatty acids important to animal's health and well-being. It should be noted that cats have an additional requirement for arachidonic acid. Although most animals can convert linoleic acid to arachidonic acid within

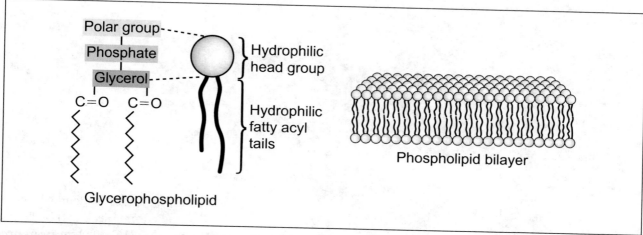

■ **Fig. 3.1.12** Orientation of phospholipids with the hydrophilic head group facing outward and the hydrophobic fatty acids facing toward the interior, producing a lipid bilayer essential to the formation of cell membranes.

the liver, cats lack a key enzyme necessary for this conversion and thus require arachidonic acid to be provided in the diet.

Phospholipids are a third type of lipid and are similar to triglycerides. Whereas triglycerides contain three fatty acids attached to a glycerol backbone, phospholipids contain only two fatty acids with a phosphate group replacing the third. Phospholipids are the primary constituents of the cell membrane and help facilitate movement of molecules into and out of the cell.

Proteins

Proteins perform a variety of functions in the body and are present as structural components in cell membranes, muscle tissue, hair, skin, and hooves. Proteins are the product of gene transcription and are the molecules of enzyme-catalyzed reactions, muscle contraction, metabolic regulation, and immune function. All cells synthesize proteins and without proteins, life could not exist. Although proteins are not a primary source of energy for tissues, they provide 4 kcal/g when catabolized.

Proteins are composed of chains of amino acids. The basic structure of an amino acid is a carboxylic acid group, an amino group (-NH$_2$), and a side chain (-R group) that differs for each of the twenty amino acids commonly found in proteins. Amino acids are linked by peptide bonds and can appear in a variety of arrangements. The linkage of two or more amino acids results in formation of a peptide. Polypeptides are made up of more than one peptide and are extended peptide chains. The term protein is reserved for large molecules of one or more polypeptides. Proteins display different levels of complexity defined by interactions within and between polypeptide chains. Primary structure is determined by the linear sequence of amino acids. Secondary structure is the result of local folding that occurs due to interactions between closely located amino acids. Tertiary structure involves more distant interactions within a polypeptide chain, and quaternary structure results from interactions between different peptide chains. Although species differences exist, the following ten amino acids are recognized as essential for most simple-stomached animals.

Arginine (Arg) plays an important role in cell division, the healing of wounds, removing ammonia from the body, immune function, and the release of hormones. Arginine is essential to the dog and cat at all stages of development. In other animals, including pigs and humans, arginine is considered conditionally essential and is required in the neonatal diet, but not the adult diet as it is produced by the urea cycle. Histidine (His) can be decarboxylated to form histamine in mammals. Histamine controls the constriction of certain blood vessels and also regulates the secretion of hydrochloric acid to the stomach. Isoleucine (Ile) is required for protein synthesis and may be degraded into simpler compounds used

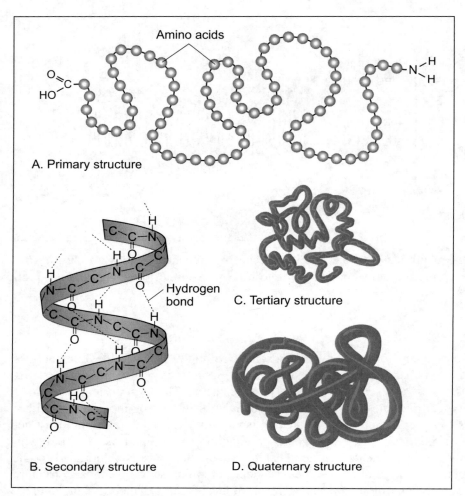

Amino acids

A. Primary structure

Hydrogen bond

C. Tertiary structure

B. Secondary structure

D. Quaternary structure

■ Fig. 3.1.13 Individual amino acids form peptide bonds for the primary structure of a protein. Further interactions of amino acids within a linear chain as a result of hydrogen bonds are responsible for the secondary structure of a protein. The tertiary structure occurs as a result of more complex attractions within the amino acid chain. When more than one amino acid chain interacts, a quaternary structure is formed. Protein structure is the ultimate determinant of protein function.

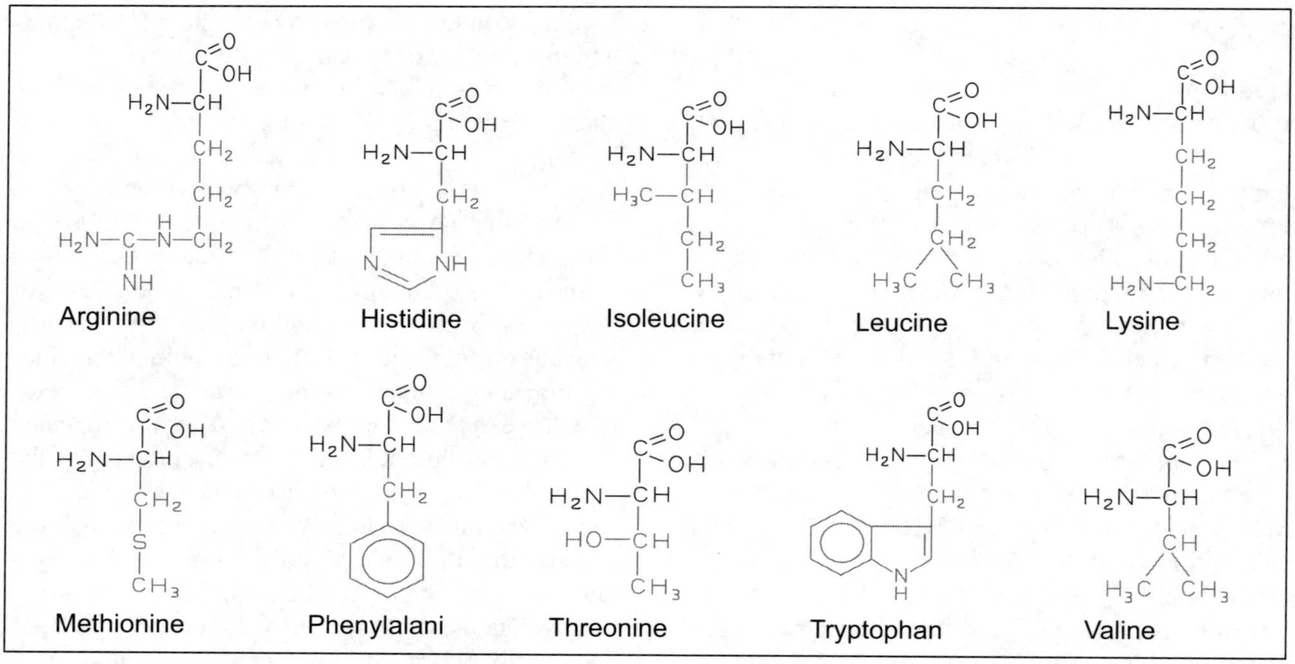

Arginine

Histidine

Isoleucine

Leucine

Lysine

Methionine

Phenylalani

Threonine

Tryptophan

Valine

■ Fig. 3.1.14   Essential amino acids first identified in rats.

for the synthesis of glucose. In a rare, inherited disorder called maple syrup urine disease, a nonfunctional enzyme in the common pathway of the degradation of the branched-chain amino acids isoleucine, leucine, and valine, causes the buildup of certain metabolites in the urine, resulting in the characteristic odor from which the disease derives its name. Leucine (Leu) is necessary for growth and may reduce protein degradation. Lysine (Lys) is an essential building block for all proteins in the body and plays a major role in calcium absorption, building of muscle and production of hormones, enzymes and antibodies. Methionine (Met) supplies sulfur, which is essential for normal metabolism and growth. It is also a methyl donor, aiding in chemical and metabolic reactions in the body. Methionine can meet the total need for sulfur-amino acids in the absence of cysteine, another sulfur containing amino acid. Phenylalanine (Phe) is unique, as it can meet an animal's complete need for both phenylalanine and tyrosine. Tyrosine is a product formed from the degradation of phenylalanine and can satisfy up to 50% of the need for both of the amino acids, though it cannot serve as the sole source. Threonine (Thr) is converted into glucose in the liver and is utilized in the stabilization of blood sugar. Tryptophan (Trp) is a precursor for niacin, the neurohormone melatonin, and the neurotransmitter serotonin, thus it is required for electrical signals between a neuron and another cell. Cataracts may develop under conditions of tryptophan deficiency. Lastly, valine (Val), although seldom used in biochemical reactions, assists in determining the three-dimensional structure of proteins due to their hydrophobic nature.

In addition to the aforementioned ten essential amino acids, poultry additionally require glycine/ serine and proline. Although the bird is capable of synthesizing these amino acids, it does not produce adequate amounts for optimal growth. Glycine (Gly) is the simplest amino acid in the body. It acts as an inhibitory neurotransmitter in the central nervous system and is important in the synthesis of proteins, peptides, adenosine triphosphate (ATP), nucleic acids, hemoglobin, glucose, glycogen, and other amino acids. Serine (Ser) is found in the active sites of some enzymes, including chymotrypsin and trypsin and thereby plays an important role in their catalytic function. Glycine and serine are interchangeable, therefore either amino acid can be used to synthesize the other, and a requirement for the individual amino acid is not established. Proline (Pro) is a major building block of collagen, and hydroxylation of proline increases the conformational stability of collagen.

The quasi-amino acid taurine is essential for cats. Taurine is a sulfur-containing compound derived from cysteine. It is not a component of proteins, but exists as a free compound that is necessary for normal cardiac muscle function, reproduction, formation of bile salts for digestion, and vision. Lack of dietary taurine in feline diets is associated with irreversible blindness.

While the remaining amino acids are components of proteins, they are considered nonessential due to adequate de novo synthesis, or synthesis by the body.

Adequate concentrations of the amino acids must be available for protein synthesis to occur. When the amount of an amino acid supplied by the diet is not sufficient to meet the animal's requirement for protein synthesis, the amino acid is said to be limiting. The first-limiting amino acid is the amino acid that is present in a diet in the least

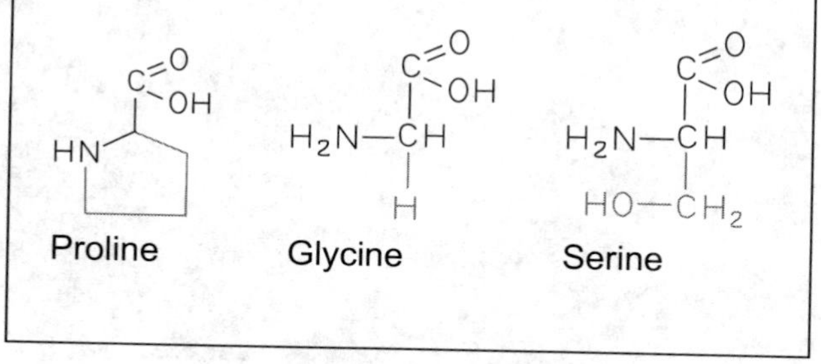

■ **Fig. 3.1.15** Additional amino acids considered essential in poultry.

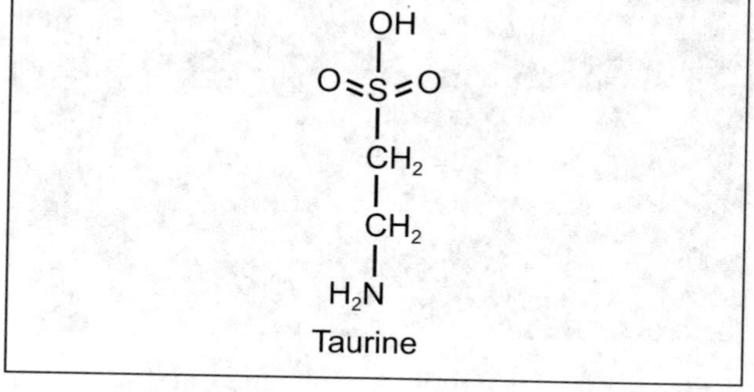

■ **Fig. 3.1.16** Taurine, a quasi-amino acid essential for felines.

amount in relation to the animal's need for that particular amino acid. The lack of availability of that amino acid in the diet restricts the performance of the animal as it limits the use of all amino acids in synthesizing a protein. For example, the limiting amino acid of corn is lysine, with tryptophan a close second. On the other hand, soybean meal is deficient in methionine-cysteine, but is rich in lysine and tryptophan. In this case, if both of corn and soybean meal were fed, the animal would be provided with an adequate balance of amino acids.

Vitamins

Vitamins are a group of organic substances that are required in relatively small amounts and are essential for life. Each vitamin has its own specific function, and the lack of a certain vitamin in the diet can cause specific deficiency symptoms that may ultimately lead to the death of the animal. Vitamins can be divided into fat soluble and water soluble based on their solubility properties.

The fat soluble vitamins include vitamins A, D, E, and K. Vitamin A is required for night vision, epithelial cells, and bone growth and remodeling. It is important for reproduction and also appears to protect against cancer. Deficiency symptoms include night blindness, poor growth, reproductive failure, reduced egg production, inadequate bone remodeling, swollen and/or stiff joints, rough coat, and hyperkeratosis. Vitamin D promotes calcium and phosphorus absorption which is important for bone mineralization. Exposure to direct sunlight promotes conversion of cholesterol to Vitamin D; there-

fore animals exposed to direct sunlight may not require dietary sources of vitamin D. Deficiency symptoms include rickets in growing animals, osteomalacia; osteoporosis, reduced egg production, and soft egg shells. Vitamin E is an antioxidant that is important in cell membrane maintenance and required for proper muscle structure and normal reproductive function. Deficiency symptoms include muscular dystrophy, reproductive failure, and white muscle disease. Vitamin K is required for normal blood coagulation. It is specifically required for the synthesis of prothrombin, a coagulating agent, in the liver. Deficiency symptoms include reduced blood coagulation in response to diminished concentrations of prothrombin, and association with spontaneous hemorrhages. Dicoumarol (a derivative of coumarin) is a natural antagonist to vitamin K that was discovered in damaged sweet clover hay by researchers at the University of Wisconsin. The anticoagulating properties of dicoumarol are useful in the medical profession in the prevention of blood clots. Dicoumarol also is effective as a component of rat poison. Exposed animals hemorrhage or bleed through the capillaries, which is the cause of death.

The remaining vitamins are classified as water soluble. Ascorbic acid (Vitamin C) plays a role in collagen formation and is involved in Vitamin E conservation. Many animals can synthesize vitamin C, but it must be provided in the diet for primates, humans, and guinea pigs. Deficiency symptoms include scurvy, anemia, hemorrhaging, spongy gums, weight loss, swollen joints, and structural defects in bone, teeth, cartilage, connective tissues, and mus-

■ **Fig. 3.1.17** Vitamin A deficiency and resulting hyperkeratosis. (Image courtesy of Tony Buffington and colleagues, The Ohio State University.)

■ **Fig. 3.1.18** Vitamin D deficiency in growing lambs can lead to the development of rickets. (Image courtesy of Tony Buffington and colleagues, The Ohio State University.)

cles. Biotin is an essential cofactor for enzymes and is involved in lipid synthesis. Deficiency symptoms include reduced growth, hair loss, dermatitis, and bone deformities in chicks. Choline is a component of some phospholipids and is an important neurotransmitter as acetylcholine. Deficiency symptoms include kidney degeneration; fatty liver; loss of co-ordination; poor reproductive performance and lactation in swine; and bone deformities in chicks. Folic Acid (B_9) is involved in amino acid metabolism and purine formation. Deficiency symptoms include poor growth; pernicious anemia ; and leucopenia. Niacin (B_3) is a constituent of the coenzymes nicotinamide adenine dinucleotide (NAD) and nicotinamide adenine dinucleotide phosphate (NADP), important reducing agents in metabolism. Deficiency symptoms include inflammation and ulceration of the mouth, tongue, and digestive tract, as well as anorexia, irritability, diarrhea, dementia (loss of cognitive function), and dermatitis. Pantothenic acid (B_5) is a component of coenzyme A (CoA) which plays an important role in the metabolism of fatty acids. Deficiency symptoms include dermatitis, loss/greying of hair, poor growth and reproductive function, digestive disorders, spastic gait, and goose-stepping or posterior incoordination and paralysis. Riboflavin (B_2) functions in the coenzymes flavin adenine dinucleotide (FAD) and flavin mononucleotide (FMN), both of which occur in numerous enzyme systems related to energy and protein metabolism. Deficiency symptoms include dermatitis and hair loss, reduced growth rates, diarrhea, ocular lesions, and curled toe paralysis in birds. Thiamin (B_1) is a coenzyme in energy metabolism. A role in nuerological function has been determined as well. Deficiency symptoms include cardiovascular disturbances, convulsions, weakness, reduced growth rates, emaciation and anorexia, polyneuritis in chicks, and opisthotonos. Pyridoxine (B_6) is a coenzyme involved in protein and nitrogen metabolism. It also is involved in red blood cell formation and antibody production. Deficiency symptoms include convulsions in swine, hyperirritability, reduced growth rates, and pernicious anemia. Cyanocobalamin (Vitamin B_{12}) is important for red blood cell maturation. Deficiency symptoms include pernicious anemia, neurological disturbances, poor reproductive performance, and reduced growth rates. As vitamin B_{12} is important in regenerating folate, the deficiencies are often the same and adequate folate will resolve most deficiencies contributed to vitamin B_{12}.

Minerals

Minerals are inorganic, solid, crystalline chemical elements that are required by all animals. Minerals are classified as macrominerals or microminerals, a distinction that is based on the relative amounts of each that are required in the diet for normal life processes.

Macromolecules are required in greater amounts in the diet and include: calcium, phosphorus, magnesium, potassium, sodium, chlorine, and sulfur. Calcium (Ca) is essential for bone and teeth formation, blood coagulation, milk production, egg shell formation, cell permeability, and as an intracellular

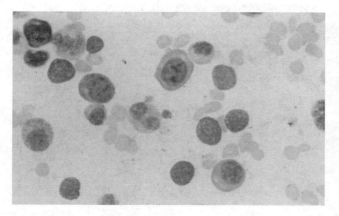 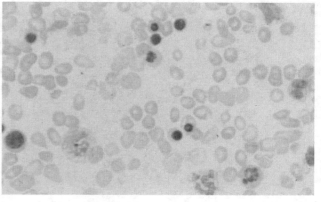

■ **Fig. 3.1.19** Megoblastic anemia (left) characterized by large, dysfunctional red blood cells following vitamin B_{12} deficiency and recovery (right) following B_{12} supplementation. (Image courtesy of Tony Buffington and colleagues, The Ohio State University.)

signal involved in transmission of nervous impulses and muscle contraction. Deficiency symptoms include rickets in young animals, osteomalacia in adults, reduced egg production, thin-shelled eggs, impaired blood clotting, and milk fever in dairy cattle. Phosphorus (P) is involved in formation of bones and teeth and is a component of the phospholipids of cell membranes. It is found in nucleic acids and influences the energy status of a cell. Deficiency symptoms include rickets in young animals, osteomalacia in adults, reduced growth rates, weight loss, and reduced egg production. Magnesium (Mg) is involved in bone formation and is involved in carbohydrate metabolism. It also is required for proper functioning of the nervous system. Deficiency symptoms include vasodilatation, hyperirritability, convulsions, loss of equilibrium, trembling, and grass tetany. Potassium (K) is a major cation of intracellular fluid and is involved in osmotic pressure, acid-base balance, and water balance. Potassium is also important for nerve impulse transmission, muscle contraction, carbohydrate metabolism, and maintenance of cardiac and renal tissue. Deficiency symptoms include lethargy with increased incidence of coma and death, diarrhea, decreased food and water intake, reduced growth and egg production in poultry, cardiac muscle abnormalities, and distended abdomen. Sodium (Na) is a cation of extracellular fluid and is involved in osmotic pressure. Sodium is critical to acid-base equilibrium and plays a role in cell permeability, muscle contraction, and nerve function. Deficiency symptoms include reduced growth rates, infertility

in males, delayed sexual maturity in females, and eye disturbances with corneal lesions. Chlorine (Cl) is a major anion of the body involved in osmotic pressure. It is essential for oxygen transport to tissues and carbon dioxide transport from tissues. Chlorine also is involved with digestive function as it combines with hydrogen to form hydrochloric acid in the stomach. Deficiency symptoms include reduced growth rates and kidney lesions. Sulfur (S) is a component of biotin and thiamine and is present in sulfur-containing amino acids, including methionine, cysteine, and taurine. A primary deficiency symptom is reduced growth rates due to the requirement of sulfur containing amino acids for protein synthesis.

The remaining minerals are required in lesser amounts in the diet and are considered microminerals or traceminerals. Chromium (Cr) is involved in lipid, protein, carbohydrate, and nucleic acid metabolism. Deficiency symptoms are rare. Cobalt (Co) is a component of vitamin B_{12} and is needed for rumen bacterial growth. Deficiency symptoms include anemia, reduced appetite in ruminants, reduced growth rates and body weight, and eventually death with prolonged deficiency. Copper (Cu) is required for bone and connective tissue metabolism, maintenance of myelin of nervous tissue, pigmentation of hair, and hemoglobin synthesis. Deficiency symptoms include loss of hair pigmentation, lack of wool, lameness, swelling of joints, fragile bones, anemia and ataxia in lambs, goats and pigs, as well as cardiovascular lesions and hemorrhages in swine, chicks, and cattle. Fluorine (F) as a gas is toxic, but

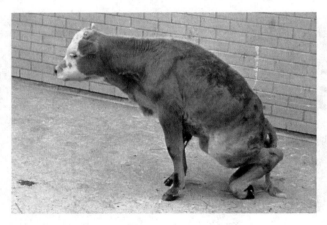

■ **Fig. 3.1.20** Posterior paralysis characteristic of copper deficiency. (Image courtesy of Tony Buffington and colleagues, The Ohio State University.)

■ **Fig. 3.1.21** Skin lesions associated with zinc deficiency. (Image courtesy of Tony Buffington and colleagues, The Ohio State University.)

inorganic compounds of fluorine such as sodium fluoride (NaF) protects teeth from decay and is suggested to slow the development of osteoporosis in mature animals. Tooth decay may occur due to deficiency; however, fluorine excess is of concern in infants and livestock. Toxicity is associated with reduced serum calcium and magnesium and is accompanied by cardiac abnormalities and nervous distress. Iron (Fe) primarily exists in the body as the heme portion of red blood cell hemoglobin and myoglobin in muscle cells. It is also a co-enzyme. Deficiency symptoms include anemia due to less than normal amounts of hemoglobin and fewer and/or smaller red blood cells resulting in shortness of breath, reduced growth rates, rough hair coats, reduced appetite, and increased susceptibility to stresses and infectious agents have been noted in swine. Iodine (I) is needed for the formation of the thyroid hormones thyroxine and triiodothryonine, both of which regulate metabolism. Deficiency symptoms include goiter, abortions and stillbirths, hairless pigs or wool-less lambs at birth, brittle hair, dry skin, slowed metabolism, irregular or suppressed estrous cycles in females, and reduced semen quality in males. Manganese (Mn) is a cofactor for several enzymes and plays a role in bone formation, growth and reproduction, amino acid and cholesterol metabolism, and fatty acid synthesis. Deficiency symptoms include reduced growth rates, testicular degeneration in males, impaired ovulation in females, and perosis in birds. Molybdenum (Mo) is involved in purine metabolism and also stimulates microbial activity in the rumen. Deficiency symptoms are uncommon. Selenium (Se) plays a role in maintaining the integrity of cellular membranes and is required for immune system function. Deficiency symptoms include mortality in poultry, liver necrosis in pigs, white muscle disease in lambs and calves when accompanied by a vitamin E deficiency which may cause sudden death if the heart is affected, reduced growth rates, reduced fertility, and paralysis. Selenium toxicity may occur as well. Toxicity is associated with reduced egg production and hatchability in poultry, while those that do hatch commonly have deformities. Livestock may develop blind staggers or alkali disease resulting in unthrifty, dull, and listless animals. Hair loss from mane and tail may occur, along with complete loss of hooves. The toxicity causes a decline in appetite which may be severe enough to cause starvation and death. Zinc (Zn) plays a role in lipid, protein, and carbohydrate metabolism and is necessary for bone and feather development, as well as immune system function. Deficiency symptoms include reduced growth rates, anorexia, poor hair or feather development and rough, thickened, or scaly skin, impaired bone formation, and delayed wound healing.

DIGESTION

"The physiologist who succeeds in penetrating deeper and deeper into the digestive canal becomes convinced that it consists of a number of chemical laboratories equipped with various mechanical devices."

—*Ivan Pavlov (1849-1936)*

A Historical Perspective

In 1750, the French scientist Reaumur discovered that substances present in the digestive tract of birds were capable of liquefying meat. Reaumur had trained a bird to swallow sponges that were regurgitated shortly after ingesting. It was the liquid recovered from these sponges that Reaumur learned could dissolve meat. The substances contained within the liquid would later be isolated and defined. Following the studies of Reaumur, an Italian scientist by the name of Spallanzani conducted digestive studies using himself as the research subject. Spallanzani would ingest small linen bags containing food. He would later recover these bags and learned that digestion occurred without mastication, as the food would disappear from the bags despite being swallowed intact. The discovery of hydrochloric acid (Prout, 1824) and pepsin (Schwann, 1835) as important digestive compounds followed. At the same time William Beaumont (1833) carried out chemical and physiological studies of digestion on a patient under his care. The patient, a trapper injured following discharge of his gun, was left with a fistula (permanent opening) into his stomach. For the pay of 150$ per year, the patient agreed to allow the experimentations of Beaumont to be performed. These studies were instrumental in revealing the nature of chemical and mechanical digestive processes.

Overview of Digestion

Most feedstuffs are consumed in forms that the contained nutrients are unavailable to the body for absorption and the feed must be broken down to smaller molecules to be absorbed. The reduction in feed size and release of nutrients for absorption is the goal of digestion and involves mechanical and chemical processes. The digestive systems of animals has evolved with their diet and the type of digestive system that an animal has will ultimately determine the types of feed the animal can consume and utilize most efficiently. The variation in types of digestive systems allows animals to occupy different places within the food chain, which reduces competition for food sources. Animals are often classified according to their diet and their digestive system. Classification according to the diet results in three groups of animals: carnivores, omnivores, and herbivores. Carnivores are flesh-eating animals, whose diet is composed primarily of non-plant material including meat, fish, or insects. Cats, birds of prey, snakes, and some fish such as sharks are all carnivores. Omnivores are animals whose diet consists of both plant and animal material. Dogs, domesticated poultry, pigs, most bears, and humans are all omnivorous species. Herbivores are animals that consume primarily plant material and have evolved specialized digestive compartments to allow the digestion of fiber. Some examples of herbivores include horses, cattle, rabbits, guinea pigs, llamas, alpacas, sheep, goats, and elephants.

Animal digestive systems are classified anatomically, and include nonruminants, ruminants, and pseudoruminants. Nonruminant animals are considered simple stomached animals that have one glandular stomach, and include pigs, cats, dogs, and humans. The avian digestive system is a modified version of the nonruminant system. Herbivores including the horse, rabbit, and elephant also are nonruminant animals that are frequently referred to as hindgut fermentors. Ruminants are animals that have a four compartmented stomach consisting of three forestomachs preceding the glandular stomach, which is analogous to that of a nonruminant. Ruminant animals include cattle, sheep, goats, and giraffes. Pseudoruminants are a sub-category of ruminant. These animals either possess modified rumens that have two forestomachs that preceed the glandular stomach such as the camelids or practice pregastric fermentation in the absence of rumination, which occurs in peccaries, kangaroos, and hippopotamus.

Prehension, Mastication, and Swallowing

Digestion begins with prehension and mastication. The mouth, including the tongue, lips, and teeth are used to obtain, hold, grind, and mix food with saliva. While the horse, llama, and alpaca use their lips to obtain food; prehension also involves the tongue of cattle and sheep, and the snout of pigs. Dentition of mammals include: the front (incisors), canine, and cheek (molars) teeth. Mammals develop a set of deciduous teeth (baby or milk teeth) that are replaced with permanent teeth as the animal ages. The types of teeth that an animal possesses are specialized for prehension and mastication according to the diet. Carnivorous animals tear food, but grinding is negligible as the canines are adapted to tear flesh and the molars are pointed to crush bone. In contrast, herbivore dentition permits extensive mastication of the food. Both lateral and vertical jaw move-

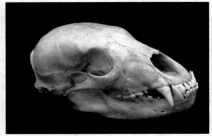

■ **Fig. 3.2.1** Animals may be classified as (left to right) carnivores, omnivores, or herbivores according to their diet. Dentition has evolved for each classification to maximize utilization of flesh and/or plant material.
(© Michael J Thompson, 2009. Under license from Shutterstock, Inc.)

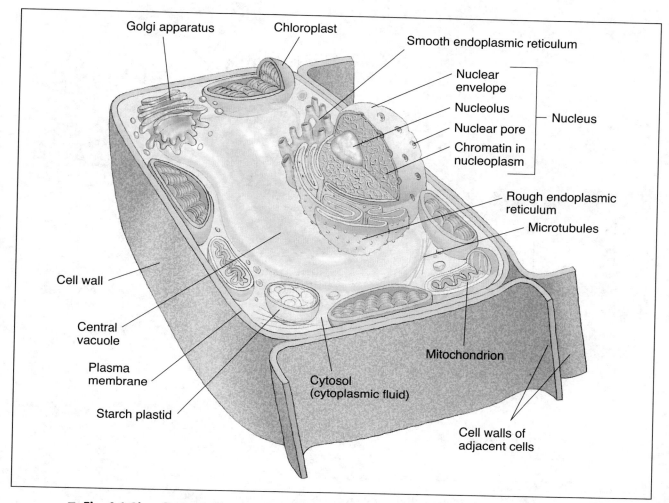

■ **Fig. 4.1.2b** General features of eukaryotic plant cell. (© Kendall Hunt Publishing Company.)

The cell wall surrounds the cell and maintains the cell's shape. In animal cells, the cell wall is absent; instead, the cytoskeleton helps maintain shape. A typical cell is not visible to the naked eye and detailed observation of cells has relied on microscopy.

Cell Composition

All cells have a similar chemical composition. The largest constituent of the cell is water, representing 60–65% of cell volume and the majority of water within a living organism is found within the cell (approximately 40% of body weight). Water acts as a solvent and is an essential constituent of many cellular processes.

Lipids are the primary components of the cell membrane and are arranged in a double layer, called a bilayer. The lipid bilayer defines the outer boundaries of the cell and serves as an impermeable barrier to the passage of most water-soluble molecules. The lipid bilayer that defines the cell is considered fluid with assemblies of carbohydrates and proteins. This dynamic property of the cell membrane is described by the Fluid Mosaic Model.

Many cellular processes are ultimately carried out by proteins. The three dimensional conformation of the protein determines the proteins biological function to regulate shape and strength of tissues, movement in muscle cells, and cellular metabolism. Proteins of cellular membranes are important mediators of cell to cell communication

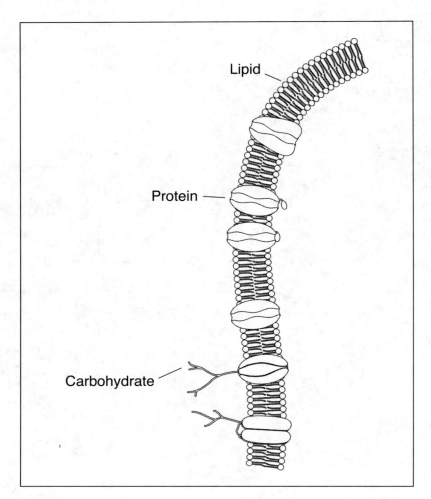

Lipid

Protein —

Carbohydrate —

■ **Fig. 4.1.3** The lipid bilayer is a primary structural feature of cell membranes. It is said to be fluid as the hydrophobic lipid components move laterally through the membrane and mosaic as it contains proteins, carbohydrates, and other molecules. These dynamic features of the cell membrane led to the fluid mosaic model as a way to describe the functional properties of the cell membrane.

as protein hormones, cell receptors, and transporters of other substances. The instructions for the production of cellular proteins are contained within the cells genetic material or deoxyribonucleic acid (DNA).

Each of the two helical strands that compose DNA consists of three chemical components: phosphate, deoxyribose (a five carbon sugar), and four nitrogenous bases assembled into nucleotides. The four nitrogenous bases are adenine, guanine, cytosine, and thymine. Adenine and guanine are purines, which are a class of chemicals that have a double-ring structure. Cytosine and thymine belong to a class of chemicals with a single-ring structure called pyrimidines. Nucleotides are often referred to by

the first letter of the name of the base it contains; A (adenosine), G (guanosine), C (cytidine), or T (thymidine) and form phosphodiester bonds between the deoxyribose sugar of one nucleotide and the phosphate of a second nucleotide. The two strands of DNA are held together by hydrogen bonds between the nitrogenous bases present on each chain. According to Chargaff's rules there are only two possible pairs of bases, that is: adenine base pairs with thymine, and guanine base pairs with cytosine. The two bases in a pair are said to be complementary, meaning that they will only bond to each other and not to either of the other two bases.

Sequences of nucleotides that serve as the precursors of proteins are known as genes. Various com-

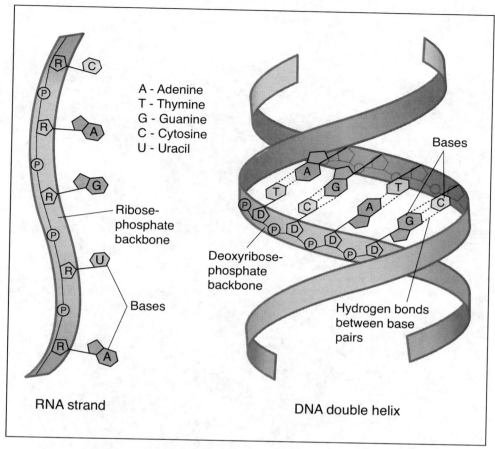

A - Adenine
T - Thymine
G - Guanine
C - Cytosine
U - Uracil

Ribose-
phosphate
backbone

Bases

RNA strand

Bases

Deoxyribose-
phosphate
backbone

Hydrogen bonds
between base
pairs

DNA double helix

■ **Fig. 4.1.4**   General features of DNA.

binations of nucleotides occur and underlie the diversity of living organisms. The process of DNA serving as the instructions for the synthesis of proteins involves the intermediate ribonucleic acids (RNA). While DNA is contained primarily within a cells nucleus, protein synthesis occurs in the endoplasmic reticulum. The process of getting the message of which protein is to be produced to the endoplasmic reticulum relies on the transfer of information into messenger RNA (mRNA). Messenger RNA is transcribed from DNA using the same complementary base pairing language observed with double stranded DNA, however, in RNA thymine is absent and is replaced by the base uracil. The mRNA that is transcribed is processed and then translated by ribosomes of the endoplasmic reticulum. Translation is the act of decoding the mRNA molecule through directing the synthesis of an amino acid chain that forms a protein. Decoding mRNA involves sequences of triplicate nucleotides termed codons. Codons code for an amino acid. Successful translation requires ribosomal RNA

(rRNA) as the site of translation and transfer RNA (tRNA) as the deliverer of amino acids to the ribosome according to the code contained within the mRNA molecule.

Carbohydrates, which consist primarily of glucose, are major components of the plant cell wall that contribute to strength. They also may be stored in a form known as starch and used to meet the energy needs of the cell. An analogous form of carbohydrate storage, referred to as glycogen, is abundant in animal cells including liver and skeletal muscle cells.

Inorganic substances are found in the cell in various quantities and are required for a variety of functions in the body. Calcium, magnesium, potassium, sodium, chloride, and phosphates are required in specific concentrations for normal nerve function and communication, as well as muscle contraction. Calcium and phosphate are both required components of bone tissue and are necessary for bone maintenance. Some minerals also act as catalysts for

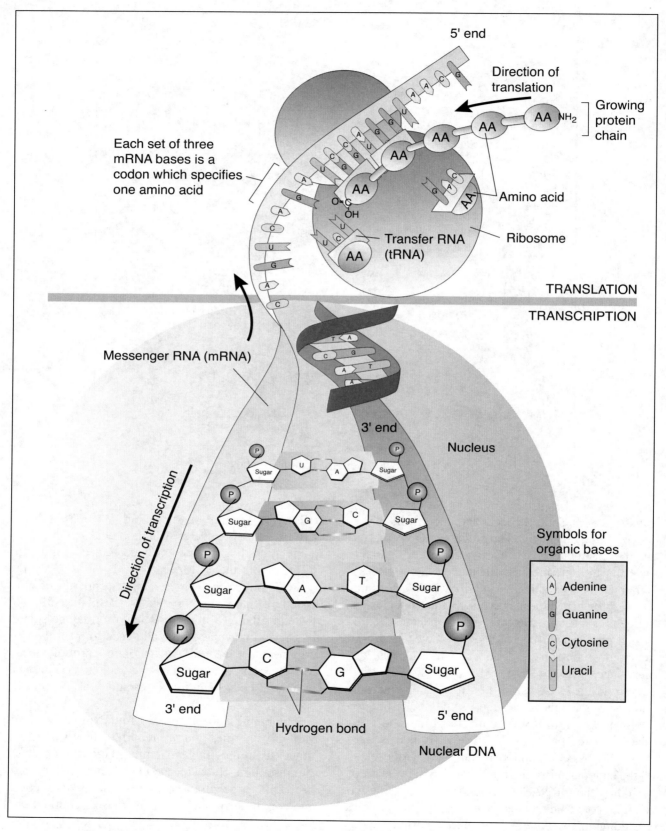

■ **Fig. 4.1.5**   Processes of transcription and translation. (© Kendall Hunt Publishing Company.)

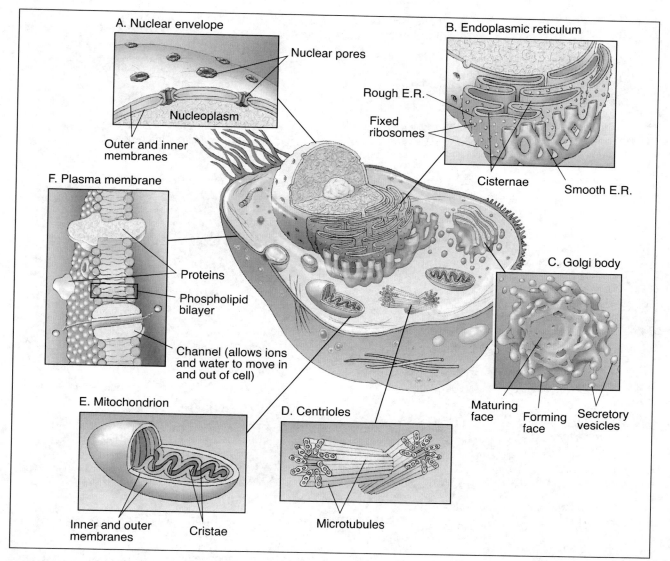

■ **Fig. 4.1.6** The plasma membrane is a lipid bilayer, consisting of a double layer of phospholipids embedded with various proteins. This is the outer boundary of the cell and functions as a selective barrier, allowing passage of oxygen, nutrients, and wastes in and out of the cell. The cytoplasm contains the cytosol (semi-fluid) and organelles. The nuclear envelope is a double membrane that encloses the nucleus and separates it from the cytoplasm. The nucleolus is a nonmembranous organelle involved in the production of ribosomes that are essential for protein synthesis. A cell may have multiple nucleoli. The nucleus contains the cell's chromosomal DNA. This chromosomal DNA is composed of chromatin, which is a complex of histone proteins and DNA. Chromatin allows for the packaging of DNA into the nucleus. Adjacent to the nucleus is the endoplasmic reticulum. Rough endoplasmic reticulum has ribosomes covering the outer surface of the membrane that function in protein synthesis. Smooth endoplasmic reticulum lacks ribosomes on its outer membrane surface. The smooth ER functions in a variety of metabolic processes including the synthesis of lipids, metabolism of carbohydrates, and detoxification of drugs and poisons. The endoplasmic reticulum works in concert with the golgi. In the golgi complex, products of the endoplasmic reticulum are modified, sorted, and then packaged for export from the cell. Mitochondria are the power plants of eukaryotic cells, using cellular respiration to convert oxygen and food/feed molecules into ATP, thereby providing energy to the cell. Centrioles are usually found in pairs in animal cells and are involved in cell division. Additional cellular organelles include lysosomes, which are digestive organelles where macromolecules are hydrolyzed and peroxisomes, which are membrane-bound vesicles that contain oxidative enzymes that generate and then degrade hydrogen peroxide and produce heat during the oxidative process.

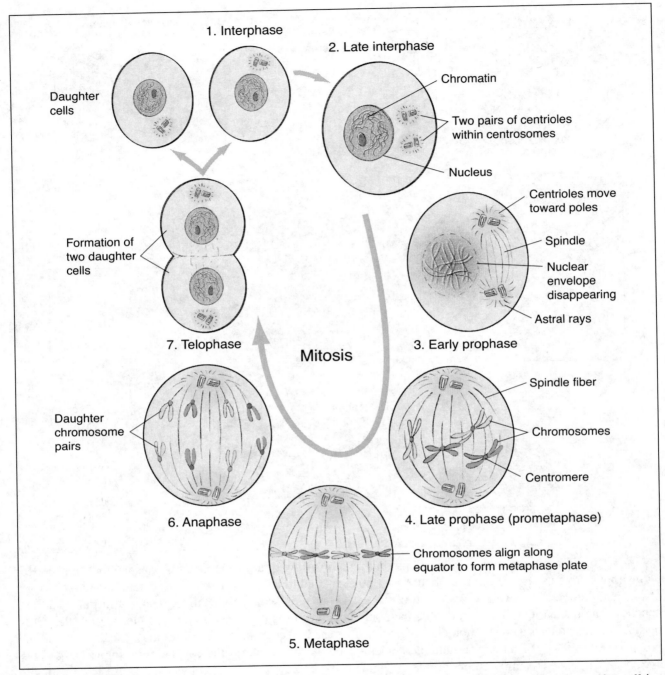

■ **Fig. 4.1.7** The process of mitosis is a complex and highly regulated event. During interphase, the cell increases in size and the DNA of the chromosomes is replicated. The centrosome is then duplicated. The chromatin fibers condense into distinguishable chromosomes during prophase. These chromosomes consist of two identical sister chromatids. The miotic spindle begins to form during this phase. It is composed of the two centrosomes and the microtubules that extend from each. Centrosomes are nonmembranous organelles that function during the cell cycle to organize the cell's microtubules. As the microtubules lengthen, the centrosomes are propelled away from one another. Prometaphase begins with the breakdown of the nuclear envelope. With this breakdown, the microtubules extend toward the center of the cell. The microtubules then attach to the kinetochore (a structure of proteins located where the two sister chromatids join). Metaphase is the longest phase of mitosis, lasting approximately twenty minutes. The centrosomes are now located at the opposite ends

(continued)

of the cell. The chromosomes are aligned on the metaphase plate, located midway between the spindle poles. The kinetochore microtubules attach the sister chromatids to the opposite poles of the spindle. Anaphase begins when the two sister chromatids of each pair separate, forming two daughter chromosomes. These chromosomes begin to move towards opposite ends of the cell as the microtubules attached to their kinetochore shorten. The nonkinetochore microtubules begin to lengthen, causing the cell to elongate. At the end of anaphase, each end of the cell has a complete set of chromosomes. Anaphase is the shortest stage of mitosis, lasting only a few minutes. During telophase, the two sets of daughter chromosomes arrive at the poles of the cell and decondense. A new nuclear envelope then begins to reassemble around each set of chromosomes from the fragments of the parent cell's envelope. The end result is the formation of two genetically identical nuclei. This is the last phase of mitosis. Following mitosis, a cleavage furrow is formed, which divides the cytoplasm in two. This division results in the formation of two daughter cells, with each cell containing one nucleus. (© Kendall Hunt Publishing Company.)

enzymes. For example, sodium and potassium activate enzymes in carbohydrate metabolism.

Cell Structure and Function

Within eukaryotic cells is an intricate network of small cellular compartments known as organelles that are integral to the basic functions of the cell and coordinate intracellular metabolism.

In complex organisms cells specialize to carry out one or more functions important to the organism's survival. Greater than two hundred types of cells are known to exist and provide the structure and function of animals. Groups of cells that coordinately regulate a specific function are tissues. In turn, a functional group of associated tissues comprise an organ and organs work together in systems. The specialized cells that constitute the structures of the organism arise from a single cell, a fertilized egg, also known as a zygote.

Shortly following fertilization, the zygote begins to replicate and divide through the process of mitosis. This phase is called cleavage, and results in the formation of many smaller cells termed blastomeres, each with its own nucleus. After numerous divisions, the cluster of cells forms a blastocyst. The blastocyst is comprised of an inner cell mass that will give rise to the embryo and an outer cell layer that develops into the placenta. The inner cell mass of the blastocyst lies at the heart of controversial embryonic stem cells. Stem cells are relatively unspecialized cells that can proliferate through mitotic division giving rise to two identical daughter cells. The daughter cells may remain stem cells or differ-

entiate, beginning the transformation into the various types of cells that comprise the body. Because there is more than one potential cell type that the stem cell may differentiate into, they are referred to as being pluripotent.

In vertebrates, this process of differentiation begins during the gastrulation stage of early embryonic development. During this stage, the cells of the blastocyst are rearranged to form a three-cell layered embryo with a primitive gut, called a gastrula. These three layers are embryonic tissues that are called the embryonic germ layers. The ectoderm layer is found on the outside of the gastrula, while the endoderm lines the embryonic digestive tract, and the mesoderm fills the space between these two layers. Every nucleus of every cell in an organism contains the same set of genes. During cell differentiation, certain genes are activated, while others are inactivated. This process is quite intricate and reliant on the cellular environment. Differentiation ultimately allows each cell to develop specific structures and perform certain functions. The various cell types that result from differentiation must replicate through mitosis. This proliferation of cells is necessary for the organism to grow, tissues and organs to maintain themselves, and wound healing and repair. Proliferation is a controlled cellular event; uncontrolled cellular proliferation is associated with disease states such as cancer.

Because the cell is the fundamental unit of life, the properties of the cell are synonymous with those of life. Succession of life is reliant on the whole organisms ability to grow, reproduce, and maintain physiological processes (digestion, absorption, metabolism, secretion, etc.), properties which are orchestrated at the cellular level and regulated by the chemical composition of the cell.

GENETICS

"Heredity provides for the modification of its own machinery."

—*James Baldwin (1861–1934)*

A Historical Perspective

The science of genetics arose from the desire of plant and animal breeders to attain a clear understanding of the inheritance of economically important characteristics in their orchards, fields, and flocks. In 1843, Gregor Mendel was recruited to an Augustinian monastery in Moravia to work on the problem of understanding the nature of variation in fruit trees. While fruit trees turned out to be too large and slow growing for this type of study, Mendel did find that pea plants were ideal for his experiments. Today he is famous for his study on these plants and is credited with the discovery of the mechanism of inheritance. It was previously believed that inheritance was the result of the mixing of blood or some other continuous substance, contributed by each parent of an individual. In 1866, after many years of study, Mendel proved that this was not the mode of inheritance; but instead, he found that for each characteristic he studied, an individual carried two particles, which he referred to as factors. He found that one factor is inherited

■ **Fig. 4.2.1** Domesticated from the wolf, selective breeding has transformed canines into the over four hundred specialized breeds reported today. (© Paunovic, 2009. Under license from Shutterstock, Inc.)

from the male parent and the other factor is inherited from the female parent. These factors kept their individuality in the offspring, that is, they did not blend together. He also found that when offspring produced gametes for reproduction, each of the gametes produced would contain only one of the two factors it had inherited from its parent. Today these factors are referred to as genes. The term was first used by Danish botanist Wilhelm Johannsen in 1909, and was derived from the word *pangenesis* coined by Darwin. *Pangenesis* comes from the Greek words *pan* (meaning "whole" or "encompassing") and *genesis* ("birth") or *genos* ("origin").

The Study of Genes

The study of genes and their heredity is referred to as genetics, while molecular genetics focuses on the genetic materials RNA and DNA, their structure, and how they control metabolic processes within cells. Genetics is a very important field of study, as the knowledge of genes and their actions is necessary to bring about genetic change. Life relies on the transfer of genetic information from parent to offspring. This genetic transfer is referred to as inheritance, and takes place at the time of conception. In animal breeding and production, the goal is to produce animals that excel for desired traits, while at the same time eliminating and/or reducing the occurrence of undesirable traits. Applied genetics, commonly referred to as animal breeding, is the science that aids in the goal of selecting and breeding animals to improve the population. Genetic improvement is the principle goal of nearly all animal breeders. Modern day animal species have changed remarkably from their wild ancestors due to the practices of breeding and selection.

Genes Are Organized in the Genome

The complete genetic material of an animal is referred to as its genome. The genomes of various species will differ in size. In general, the more simplistic organisms will have genomes that are substantially smaller than those of more complex, multicellular organisms. In most plants and animals, the somatic cells contain two copies of the organism's genome. These types of organisms are referred to as

diploid (2n). On the other hand, organisms that have only one copy of their genome are called haploid (n). These tend to be rather simplistic and include organisms such as fungi, algae, and bacteria.

The genome of an organism serves as the basic blueprint for the organism and contains both the

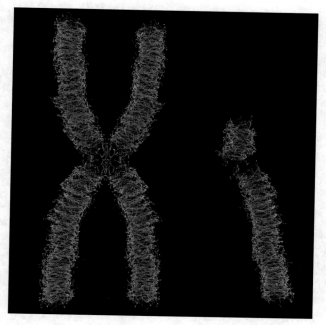

■ **Fig. 4.2.2**   The sex of a zygote is determined by chance. Every somatic cell of an organism contains a pair of sex chromosomes. In mammalian species, the female pair of sex chromosomes is XX. Males on the other hand have one X chromosome like that of the female, but the second chromosome is a Y chromosome. Females (XX) are referred to as homogametic since both of their sex chromosomes are the same, while males are referred to as heterogametic since their sex chromosomes differ. In poultry, the sexes are reversed, such that the heterogametic sex is the female and the homogametic sex is the male. As opposed to the XX and XY designations used in mammalian species, ZZ is used to designate males, while ZW is used to designate females. Since the avian female is the heterogametic sex, the female will determine the sex of the offspring, whereas in mammals, the male is the one who determines the sex. (© MichaelTaylor, 2009. Under license from Shutterstock, Inc.)

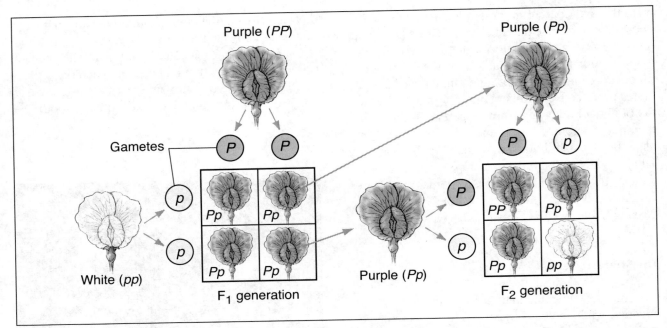

Purple (*PP*)

Purple (*Pp*)

Gametes

White (*pp*)

F₁ generation

Purple (*Pp*)

F₂ generation

■ **Fig. 4.2.3** Mendel crossed contrasting pea varieties and recorded his observations. Crossing peas with white flowers and peas with purple flowers (referred to as the parental crosses) yielded hybrid offspring (F₁ generation) with purple flowers. When the F₁ generation were allowed to self pollinate to produce the F₂ generation, the white flowers that were absent in the F₁ generation reappeared in the F₂ generation. (© Kendall Hunt Publishing Company.)

genes that code for protein and non-coding regions that do not give rise to proteins, but may serve a regulatory function. The information the genome carries essentially controls all of the biochemical life processes within the body. The genome is structured into segments of DNA, which forms long, thread-like strands called chromosomes that are located in the nucleus of every cell. Each gene in an organism will occupy a specific location on a particular chromosome, called its locus.

Chromosomes are present in pairs, with one chromosome of the pair being inherited from the female parent and the other chromosome being inherited from the male parent, which is why somatic cells are diploid. Since chromosomes occur in pairs in somatic cells, then so do genes as well, with the paired chromosomes have corresponding loci. Autosomes (non-sex chromosomes) are referred to as homologs or homologous chromosomes. Sex chromosomes are an exception to the general pattern of homologous chromosomes where males are characterized by the XY chromosomes in mammals and females the ZW chromosomes in avians.

The number of chromosomes an animal has is dependent on its species. For example, cattle have sixty chromosomes (fifty-eight autosomes and two sex chromosomes), or thirty chromosome pairs. While the number of chromosomes is known for a species, the total number of genes on a pair of chromosomes is not known, but is estimated at several hundred to a few thousand.

The various forms of a given gene on corresponding homologous chromosomes are alleles. While alleles for a particular gene do affect the same trait, different proteins may be produced, and therefore differences in the way the trait is expressed may occur. Alleles of a gene are generally represented by a letter. To differentiate between the different allelic forms of a gene, one form is often noted as an upper case letter, and the other as a lower case letter (i.e., A and a). When the alleles for a given gene are the same, it is said to be homozygous. On the other hand, when the alleles at a given locus differ or contrast one another they are referred to as heterozygous. Using the above lettering system, a gene with contrasting alleles would be represented as Aa, and a gene with the same alleles would be designated as AA or aa. The combination of alleles for a given gene is referred to as the genotype for that locus. In reference to an organism, the term genotype refers to the entire listing of the specific genes (and their alleles) carried on the chromosomes.

Inheritance

The transfer of chromosomes and their alleles from parents to their offspring is the basis of inheritance. Each parent produces reproductive cells called gametes, which are haploid and thus only one allele for each gene. Which one of the two parental alleles that ends up in a gamete is determined by the two laws of inheritance derived by Mendel. The first law is the principle of segregation, stating that alleles separate so that only one randomly chosen allele is found in any particular gamete. Mendel's second law is the principle of independent assortment, stating that during the formation of gametes, separation of a pair of genes is independent of the separation of other gene pairs. These two fundamental principles of heredity were conjectured from Mendel's early studies that involved crossing of pea plants.

Species	Number of Chromosomes
Humans	46 (23 pairs)
Cattle	60 (30 pairs)
Horses	64 (32 pairs)
Swine	38 (19 pairs)
Sheep	54 (27 pairs)
Chickens	78 (39 pairs)
Goats	60 (30 pairs)
Llamas	74 (37 pairs)
Dogs	78 (39 pairs)
Cats	38 (19 pairs)
Bison	60 (30 pairs)

Mendel's studies disproved the widely accepted notion that inheritance was a result of the blending of traits from parents. Instead, he proposed that parents contained two copies of the factors responsible for inheritance and these factors split, ie segregated, during meiosis and the formation of gametes.

Variation in chromosome number may occur due to the many processes that are required to take place for inheritance to be possible. Polyploidy is one of the possible variations and occurs when an individual inherits more than two full sets of chromosomes (one from each parent). This condition is uncommon in vertebrates, but does occur frequently in plants. Another potential variation in chromosome number is aneuploidy, in which an organism has a chromosome number that is not an exact multiple of the haploid number. Monosomy is a form of aneuploidy in which an organism is missing one chromosome from an otherwise diploid cell (2n-1). Similarly, trisomy is another form of aneuploidy where an additional chromosome is present in an otherwise diploid cell (2n+1). Monosomy is often a lethal condition, while trisomy may result in normal, or slightly abnormal development, but usually not death. Down's syndrome is a common example of trisomy in humans and is also referred to as trisomy 21, as it occurs at chromosome number 21. Trisomy is most commonly due to failure of the chromosomes to separate in meiosis, resulting in a gamete carrying two copies of that chromosome. When this gamete combines with another during fertilization, three copies of that chromosome will then be present.

Expression of Traits

According to Mendel's second law, the chromosomes of a gamete are a result of any random combination of maternal and paternal chromosomes from the parent generation, contributing to the genetic variability witnessed in a population. Following fertilization and the combining of the alleles from each gamete, the relationship between the alleles will determine which gene is expressed, ie the allele inherited with the paternal or maternal chromosome. The ways in which alleles are expressed are of great interest to animal breeders, as they play a major role in determining the visible or measurable characteristics or traits that an animal demonstrates. Dominant alleles are alleles that will be expressed over recessive alleles. Therefore, when a dominant allele is present, the characteristic it codes for will be expressed. On the other hand, a recessive allele will only be expressed when the dominant allele for that gene is not present.

Complete dominance is the form of dominance in which the trait expressed is the same for both the homozygous and heterozygous genotypes. The traits expressed for the homozygous recessive genotype is different from that of the other two genotypes. An example of this type of dominance is black and red coat color in cattle, where the allele that codes for a black coat is dominant, and an allele that codes for a red coat is recessive. Therefore, if an animal receives a dominant allele from each parent, it will have a black coat; likewise, an animal that receives both a dominant allele from one parent and a recessive allele from the other parent will also have a black coat. Only when the animal inherits a recessive allele from each parent will it have a red coat. This is best illustrated using a Punnett square.

People often think of dominant alleles as being "good" and recessive alleles as being "bad." It is argued that dominant alleles offer a competitive advantage, whereas recessive alleles are deleterious to the animals survival. While several genetic disorders are associated with recessive alleles (often associated with enzyme function), the red coat color of angus cattle is a desirable trait that occurs as a result of a recessive gene. Similarly, not all dominant traits are beneficial. The Manx breed of cat is characterized as being tailless. The tailless trait is a result of the shortening of the spine associated with a dominant gene and is found in cats with the heterozygous genotype. The homozygous dominant genotype, however, is considered an embryonic lethal genotype; whereas, homozygous recessive animals are born with tails. In mating two Manx cats, one can predict that 25% of the offspring would have tails, 50% of the offspring would be tailless, and 25% of the offspring would die in-utero. A similar mode of inheritance is noted for dwarfism in Dexter cattle, which is also associated with embryonic lethality for homozygous dominant carriers.

Co-dominance or no dominance can occur when neither allele masks the other, and both are expressed when they are present in the heterozygous state. The animal will have characteristics intermediate of the two homozygous genotypes; however, it will always more closely resemble the homozygous dominant trait. An example of this is roan coat color in shorthorn cattle. This occurs when an animal in-

■ **Fig. 4.2.4**   During meiosis, the chromosome set is reduced from diploid to haploid. This reduction is to compensate for the doubling of the chromosome set that occurs during fertilization. Meiosis is similar to mitosis as it is also preceded by the replication of chromosomes. However, meiosis is different in that this single replication is followed by two consecutive cell divisions referred to as meiosis I and meiosis II, which give rise to haploid cells, each with only half as many chromosomes as the parent cell. During the first phase of meiosis, prophase I, the chromosomes condense. Homologous chromosomes align precisely and are loosely paired. This phase generally occupies 90% of the time required for meiosis. At the end of prophase I, the homologous pairs begin to move towards the metaphase plate. During metaphase I the chromosome pairs align along the metaphase plate. Anaphase I begins with the movement of homologous chromosomes to opposite poles. The sister chromatids (copies of DNA) will remain attached at the centromere as they move together toward the same pole. During telophase I, each chromosome is composed of sister chromatids and each half of the cell contains a haploid set of chromosomes (ie, there is one chromosome, but two chromatids). Cytokinesis occurs simultaneously with telophase I and forms two haploid daughter cells by dividing the cell in half, marking the end of meiosis I. Meiosis II begins with prophase II, during which time the spindle apparatus forms and the chromatids begin moving towards the metaphase II plate. During metaphase II the chromosomes are lined up along the metaphase plate as in mitosis. In Anaphase II, the sister chromatids separate as they more toward opposite poles. During Telophase II, the nuclei of the two cells form and the chromosomes begin to decondense. Cytokinesis follows directly, resulting in the production of four haploid daughter cells from the meiotic division of one parent cell.

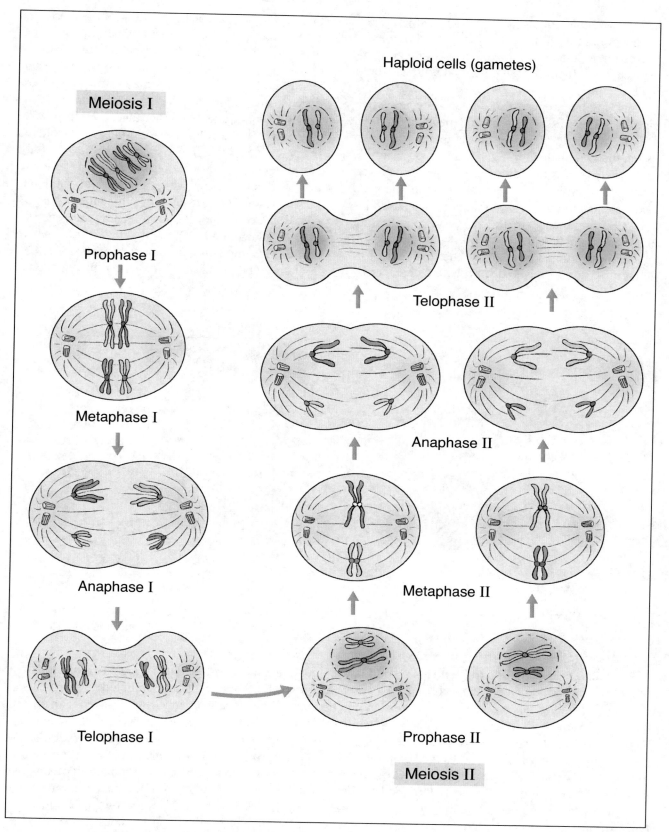

Fig. 4.2.4 See caption on previous page. (© Kendall Hunt Publishing Company.)

herits one allele coding for red coat color, and one allele coding for white coat color. Instead of one allele being dominant over the other, they are both expressed, resulting in a roan color pattern that is both red and white.

In-complete or partial dominance occurs when an allele is expressed in a dose dependant manner. This results in an offspring that is intermediate between the two alleles for a given trait. For example, if one were to cross a red flower with a white flower, incomplete dominance would result in pink flowers. Likewise, palomino coat color in horses is due to incomplete dominance in the offspring of chestnut and cremello mated horses.

While dominance involves the interaction of genes at a single locus to determine the characteristics of an animal, epistasis is a type of interaction among genes at different loci to determine gene expression. In this case, the expression of a gene at one locus will depend on the alleles present at one or more other loci. Epistasis may result in gene expression that appears quite different than what the principles of Mendelian inheritance would predict. Epistasis plays a role in determining coat color in many species, including Labrador Retrievers. Labs can either be yellow, chocolate, or black. These colors are determined by genes at two loci, the black (B) locus and the extension of pigmentation (E) locus. Black coat color is determined by the genotype BXEX, chocolate bbEX, and yellow XXee; where X indicates that either dominant or recessive alleles could be substituted without altering the phenotype.

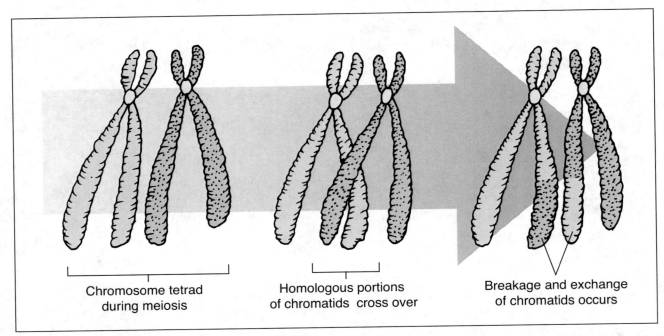

Chromosome tetrad during meiosis

Homologous portions of chromatids cross over

Breakage and exchange of chromatids occurs

■ **Fig. 4.2.5**   An exception to Mendel's second law is due to linkage. Linkage occurs when two or more loci of interest are located on the same chromosome. Since chromosomes, not genes, are separated during meiosis, most of the time, genes on the same chromosome will end up in the same gamete. Crossing-over is an exception to this same chromosome, same gamete tendency. The process of crossing over is a reciprocal exchange of chromosome segments between homologs that occurs during meiosis before the chromosomes are separated to form gametes. These exchanged genes then recombine to form a new combination of genes on a chromosome in the process of recombination. Cross-over events are rather common and the probability of any two linked loci recombining is mainly determined by the distance between the two loci. Loci that are far apart are more likely to recombine than loci that are close together. This is because there is a very low probability of a break occurring between loci that are close together in comparison to loci that are farther apart. (© Kendall Hunt Publishing Company.)

Note that the expression of the genes at the black locus is dependent on the alleles present at the extension locus. As long as there is the dominant E allele, then the lab will be black or chocolate, depending on the alleles at the black locus; however, if there are two recessive ee alleles at the extension locus, no matter what alleles are present at the black locus, the lab will be yellow.

Sex-Related Inheritance

Not all traits are confined to autosomes. Sex-linked inheritance refers to traits that are present on the X chromosome. While males have a Y chromosome, it is argued that it does not contribute to sex-linked inheritance as the few genes located to this chromosome are not expressed in observable traits. As stated earlier, sex chromosomes are an exception to the rule that chromosomes exist as homologous pairs. In mammalian males with XY chromosomes, there is only one copy of the majority of genes as there are no corresponding loci of the Y chromosome for the genes of the X chromosome. Sex-linked genes are those genes associated with regions of the X chro-

mosome that do not have corresponding loci on the Y chromosome. Genes that are X-linked can be passed on to either male or female offspring, since both will inherit at least one X chromosome.

An example of an X-linked trait is the orange and black coloration in tortoiseshell and calico cats. Tortoiseshell cats have a mixture of colors in their coat appearing in patches, always with some orange, and generally with white and black coloration. If there is a substantial amount of white, the cat is considered to be calico. Tortoiseshell cats are females, except for very rare exceptions. This is due to the fact that the locus for orange and black coloration is present on the X chromosome. Black coloration occurs with the genotype X^BX^B for females and X^BY for males. Orange coloration occurs with the genotypes X^OX^O for females and X^OY for males. The coat of the tortoiseshell cat occurs with the genotype X^BX^O and results when one X chromosome is randomly inactivated through the formation of a bar body. Inactivation of the X chromosome occurs during early embryonic development and since it is a random event either the X^B or X^O allele will be inactivated. This allele will remain inactive during mitosis, thus as cells divide, they will carry the

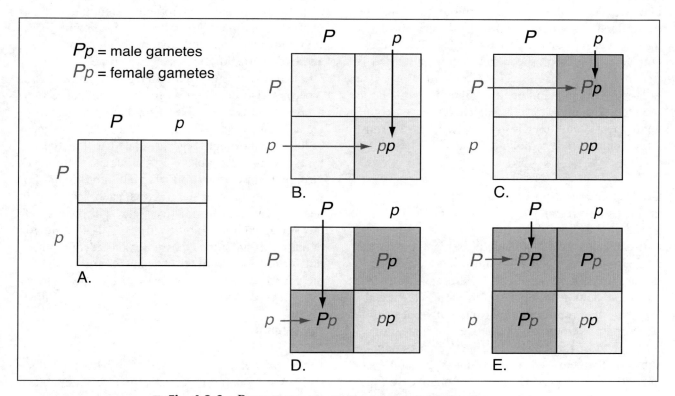

■ **Fig. 4.2.6**   Punnett square. (© Kendall Hunt Publishing Company.)

Fig. 4.2.7 A salient feature of the Manx cat is the absence of the tail, which results from an autosomal dominant gene. (© Cheryl Kunde, 2009. Under license from Shutterstock, Inc.)

Predicted Offspring of Black Lab Matings

		Black Dam (BbEe)			
		BE	Be	bE	be
Black Sire (BbEe)	B E	BBEE black	BBEe black	BbEE black	BbEe black
	B e	BBEe black	BBee yellow	BbEe black	Bbee yellow
	b E	BeEE black	BbEe black	bbEE chocolate	bbEe chocolate
	b e	BeEe black	Bbee yellow	bbEe chocolate	bbee chocolate

allele for either black or orange giving rise to patches of color.

Sex-linked should not be mistaken with sex-limited, which are traits that are limited to only one sex. Examples include milk production in females and cryptorchidism in males. While both sexes carry genes for sex limited traits, only one sex is capable of expression of the trait. Furthermore, traits may be sex-influenced, where reciprocal expression of the trait occurs in males compared to females. For example, in breeds of sheep the allele for horned is dominant to the recessive form for polled (absence of horns) in males. In females, polled is dominant to the recessive allele for horned. Therefore, when the genotype is heterozygous males will have horns, while females will be polled.

Qualitative and Quantitative Traits and the Phenotype

Ultimately, an animal's value is associated with the expression of the genotype into traits of economic importance. These visible or measurable traits that an animal demonstrates are referred to as the phenotype and may represent either qualitative or quantitative measurements. Qualitative (or categorical) traits are those that can be described, but can only be subjectively measured. These traits are generally expressed in categories. Examples of qualitative traits include coat color and presence of horns. These

types of traits are usually controlled by a relatively few genes and are called simply-inherited traits. In comparison, quantitative traits are traits that can be numerically measured as they show continuous (numerical) expression. These traits are often controlled by many different genes (polygenic), making it difficult to pinpoint the contribution of a specific gene to the animal's phenotype. Examples of quantitative traits include: milk yield; calving ease; weaning, yearling, and mature weight; litter size; and backfat thickness.

The phenotype is not based solely on the genotype, but also is reliant on the environment; a relationship that is represented as: genotype + environment = phenotype. The extent that the environment influences the phenotype is related to the type of trait. Qualitative traits are less influenced by the environment in comparison to quantitative traits. For example, environmental factors such as climate, health, management practices, etc. will have an effect on the animal's ability to reach its full genetic potential. If an animal possesses the genetic potential for enhanced growth, but nutrition is withheld, the genetic potential for growth will not be realized.

Heritability

While phenotype is determined by both genetics and environment, only the genetic effects are inherited. Heritability is a measure of the strength of the

■ **Fig. 4.2.8** Coat color of tortoise shell cats is an example of X-linked traits. (© Melissa Ann Kilhenny, 2009. Under license from Shutterstock, Inc.)

relationship between phenotypic values (performance) and breeding values (value of genes to the progeny) for a trait in a population. Simply put, heritability is the proportion of phenotypic variation that can be passed from parent to offspring. In attempts to determine how much progress can be made in traits from generation to generation, heritability estimates have been made for traits of importance in animal species. Heritability is not constant and may vary from one population of animals to the next and even within a population over time.

Heritability values range from zero to one and can be thought of as a percentage or proportion. Traits ranging in value from 0–0.2 are considered to be lowly heritable. Reproductive traits are generally lowly heritable traits. Moderately heritable traits, such as growth traits are those with values ranging from 0.2–0.4. Highly heritable traits range from 0.4–0.6 and include carcass merit traits. Lowly heritable traits do not demonstrate much change from generation to generation with the use of selection. However, traits that are highly heritable can be selected for and will result in a greater degree of change in less time.

Heritability is used to estimate the value of an individual as a parent through transmitting desirable genes to the offspring and can be used to determine the predicted rate for genetic progress. Genetic progress from one generation to the next is predicted by: *selection differential x heritability,* where selection differential represents the phenotypic advantage of the animals chosen to be parents in relation to the average for the population. Accordingly, the annual rate for genetic progress is predicted by: (*selection differential x heritability)/generation interval,* where generation interval represents the average period of time between the birth of one generation and the birth of the subsequent generation. Genetic progress can therefore be achieved more rapidly in animals that have shorter generation intervals compared to animals with longer generation intervals. This has contributed to the use of rodents and chickens in multi-generational studies to examine the role of genes in disease processes.

Population Genetics

To be able to make genetic progress in animal populations, one must know how often particular genes of interest occur in a population. Within a population, the proportion of loci that contain a particular allele is referred to as gene frequency. In turn, the relative occurrence of a particular genotype within a population is referred to as genotypic frequency and the relative occurrence of a particular phenotype is referred to as the phenotypic frequency. Population genetics is the study of how allele and genotypic frequencies change, and thus influence genetic merit within a population. In population genetics, large numbers of observations are involved and genes are viewed collectively.

If no evolutionary forces are at work to change genotypic frequencies, and a population is randomly mating, then it would be expected that gene and genotypic frequencies would remain constant from generation to succeeding generation. A state of constant gene and genotypic frequencies such as this is referred to as Hardy-Weinberg equilibrium. For a population to be in Hardy-Weinberg equilibrium, it must meet five requirements: large population size, random mating, no migration, no mutation, and no selection. The formula for the Hardy-Weinberg equilibrium equation is as follows:

$$p + q = 1$$

or it can be extended as:

$$p^2 + 2pq + q^2 = 1$$

Here, p represents the frequency of dominant alleles, while q represents the frequency of recessive alleles. This being the case, p^2 represents the frequency of homozygous dominant genotypes, 2pq represents the frequency of heterozygote genotypes, and q^2 represents the frequency of homozygous recessive genotypes. Due to the requirements of Hardy-Weinberg equilibrium, essentially no populations will exist in Hardy-Weinberg equilibrium.

A major reason that domesticated animals are not in Hardy-Weinberg equilibrium is due to the fact that they experience a great deal of selection. Whereas natural selection is the differential success in the reproduction of different phenotypes due to the interaction of an organism and its environment and is independent of deliberate human control, artificial selection is under human control. Under the premise of natural selection, animals with favorable phenotypes are more suited and have greater opportunity to mate than others, thus favorable traits become more common over successive generations. Artificial selection is based on management decisions of breeders. Animals with undesirable phenotypes are culled, while superior replacements are chosen to alter the gene frequency of a herd to achieve the desired phenotype.

Gene and genotypic frequencies also are altered by mutations, changes in the chemical composition of a gene that alters DNA. Mutations result in the production of new alleles and while they are considered to occur rarely within a population, they prevent Hardy-Weinberg equilibrium from being obtained within a population. A variety of mutations may occur, including nucleotide base substitutions, deletions, and insertions. Substitutions may occur as point mutations, which are when only one nucleotide base pair is changed. Although point mutations may be silent mutations, in which the nucleotide base substitution still codes for the same amino acid due to the redundancy of the genetic code, missense and nonsense mutations may occur as well. If the resulting codon codes for a different amino acid than the original gene sequence, the mutation is then referred to as a missense mutation. Missense mutations are called such because the code still makes sense (gives rise to an amino acid), although not necessarily the right sense. When a point mutation results in a codon that normally encodes an amino acid becoming a stop codon, this is called a nonsense mutation. A nonsense mutation

causes translation to be terminated prematurely, and the resulting polypeptide will be shorter than the polypeptide encoded by the normal gene.

Insertions and deletions are another type of mutation in which nucleotide base pairs are added or lost within a gene. When base pairs are not added or deleted in multiples of three, the result is a frameshift mutation. As mRNA is read as a series of nucleotide triplets (codons) during translation, the insertion or deletion of nucleotides may alter the reading frame. All of the nucleotides downstream from the mutation will be improperly grouped, and therefore will code for the wrong amino acid sequence. This will likely result in a nonfunctional protein unless the frameshift is near the end of the gene.

While mutations can ultimately improve protein function, they also may lead to nonfunctional proteins. Genetic, or hereditary, disorders often result when a mutation has an adverse effect on the phenotype of an organism. An example of a genetic disorder due to a mutation is muscular hypertrophy in callipyge sheep. A point mutation, as a result of an adenine to guanine substitution on chromosome 18, results in extreme muscle growth and compromised tenderness. Similarly, nucleotide deletions in the myostatin gene have contributed to the double muscling phenotype in cattle (11 nucleotide base pair deletion) and to the bully phenotype (two nucleotide base pair deletion) in whippets.

Mating Systems for Genetic Change

There are two tools used by animal breeders to make genetic change in a herd. They are selection and mating. Selection is the process of determining which animals will become parents, as well as how many offspring or litters they produce and how long they will remain in the breeding population. Mating is the process of determining which selected males will be bred to which selected females. The genetic variation among animals allows breeders to select superior animals to be the parents of the next generation. There are a variety of ways to select and mate these animals, referred to as mating systems.

Random mating is a mating system in which selected animals are allowed to mate at random. Random mating does not mean mating without selection; it simply means that the mating of selected breeding stock is not controlled. All of the males and females are combined and kept together so that each male has an equal opportunity to mate with each female. Since an entire herd or flock can be handled as a single unit during the breeding season, random mating demands less labor than other mating systems. When breed registration is required, as with purebred animals, random mating cannot be used with more than one male. This is due to the fact that both the sire and dam of an animal must be recorded for an animal to be registered. Registration is usually not as important in commercial herds and therefore random mating is more commonly used.

Inbreeding is the mating of closely related animals within a breed. The degree of inbreeding increases with the mating of more closely related animals. Nearly all purebred animals are inbred to some extent. Inbreeding is used to concentrate the desired genes known to be present in a superior animal, and in turn increase homozygosity and thus predictability for desired traits in offspring. This increase in homozygosity is due to the fact that relatives are more likely to carry the same alleles than animals selected at random from the species. When this is practiced in a population, variation in the genes existing in the population will decrease. Unfortunately, as homozygosity increases, it will increase the chances of detrimental recessive genes being expressed and decrease fitness or performance, known as inbreeding depression. Since inbreeding can lead to the expression of detrimental genes, it is important to carefully control inbreeding to allow the desired genes to be expressed, while, at the same time, minimizing the expression of undesirable genes and inbreeding depression. Inbreeding is not generally recommended for most animal production systems due to the risk of inbreeding depression.

A less restrictive form of inbreeding is linebreeding. It is the mating of animals that have one common ancestor appearing multiple times, at least three to four generations removed in the pedigree. Every breed of animal is linebred to some extent due to the fact that animals of each breed trace back to common ancestors. In comparing inbreeding to linebreeding, inbreeding would be the mating of a sire to the daughter, while an example of linebreeding would be the mating of a grandsire to the granddaughter. Knowledge of mating systems and detailed pedigrees are required to prevent linebreeding from becoming inbreeding.

■ **Fig. 4.2.9**   Artificial selection is responsible for the distinct features of breeds evidenced in animal populations and ensures that desired characteristics are continued in subsequent generations. (© Eric Isselée, 2009. Under license from Shutterstock, Inc.)

Outbreeding, or outcrossing, is the mating of less closely related individuals when compared to the average of the population and can be used to introduce new genetic material into a population. This mating system is considered the opposite of inbreeding, as the individuals mated are generally unrelated for four to six generations. Outbreeding results in an increase in heterozygous gene pairs. This increase in heterozygosity reduces the chances of the animal expressing undesirable recessive genes and increases the performance of an animal relative to the performance of its parents. This superiority of an outbred animal is referred to as heterosis or hybrid vigor. A type of outbreeding referred to as crossbreeding creates an even greater level of heterosis than outbreeding. Crossbreeding is defined by the mating of two different breeds of animals. Because animals within a breed have a greater degree of homozygosity, a cross between two breeds will increase heterozygosity in the offspring. The combining of different alleles from different breeds is what contributes to the degree of heterosis. Traits that are lowly heritable, such as reproductive traits, demonstrate the greatest levels of heterosis. Moderately heritable traits only show moderate levels of heterosis, including growth rates. Highly heritable traits demonstrate low levels of heterosis. Heterosis also declines with subsequent generations. It is greatest in the first generation and

vas deferens is to transport sperm. The transport is facilitated by contractions of smooth muscle in the walls of the vas deferens. The urethra is a single excretory duct extending from the opening of the urinary bladder to the end of the penis. The urethra functions to expel urine and semen.

Accessory Sex Glands

Male accessory sex glands are located along the pelvic portion of the urethra and produce the majority of the ejaculate, or semen, which is the medium for the transport of the sperm. The secretions produced by these glands include buffers, nutrients, and inorganic ions required to assure optimal motility and fertility of the sperm. Semen protects the sperm by aiding in the neutralization of the acidic environment present in the female genital tract. These glands have secretory ducts that open into the urethra. The accessory sex glands include the ampullae, vesicular glands, prostate gland, and bulbourethral glands. The ampullae are enlargements of the vas deferens located just before the urethra. They are the first glands to add fluid to the ejaculate. Ampullae are not present in all species, including swine. The vesicular glands (seminal vesicles) are a pair of lobular glands with a grape cluster appearance. These glands are located near the bladder. The vesicular glands greatly contribute to the fluid volume of semen. The fluid produced by these glands contains fructose and sorbitol, which are not found in any of

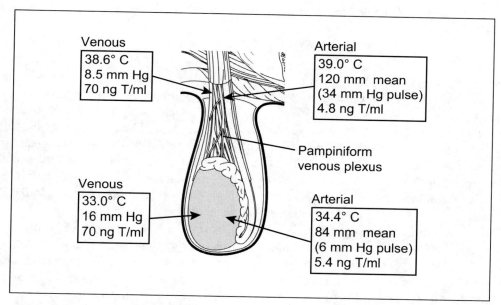

Venous
38.6° C
8.5 mm Hg
70 ng T/ml

Arterial
39.0° C
120 mm mean
(34 mm Hg pulse)
4.8 ng T/ml

Pampiniform venous plexus

Venous
33.0° C
16 mm Hg
70 ng T/ml

Arterial
34.4° C
84 mm mean
(6 mm Hg pulse)
5.4 ng T/ml

■ **Fig. 5.5** It is important that the scrotum is kept cool, as high temperatures can cause the degeneration of cells lining the seminiferous tubules, resulting in infertility. If the normal temperature is restored before total degeneration of the cells, then fertility can be restored as well, though this may take a few weeks. Ideally, the testes should be 4–6° C cooler than the normal body temperature of the animal. Thermosensors in the scrotum can detect outside temperature and then initiate the appropriate physiological reactions. One of these reactions is to either draw the testes closer to the body as temperatures fall or to let them be farther away from the body as temperatures rise. There are two muscles involved in this process. One is a smooth muscle called the tunica dartos which lines the scrotum. The other is the external cremaster, a striated muscle that is located around the spermatic cord. The scrotum also contains a specialized vascular system referred to as the pampiniform plexus. The pampiniform plexus is a countercurrent blood supply in which cooler venous blood leaving the testes cools the warmer arterial blood entering the testes.

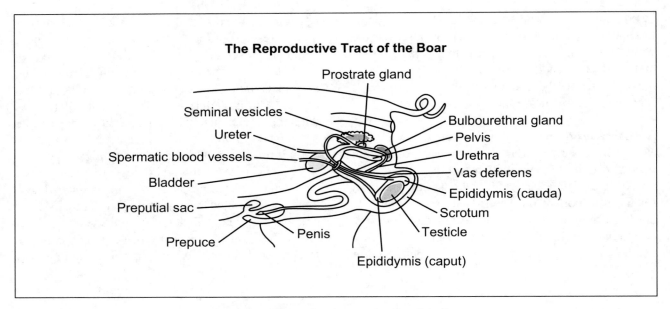

Fig. 5.6   Reproductive anatomy of the boar.

the other glandular secretions. Both fructose and sorbitol are major sources of energy for sperm. The prostate gland is a single gland located where the vas deferens and the urethra converge in some species, including the horse. In other species the prostate gland is embedded in the muscular wall of the urethra. The prostate gland contributes little to the fluid volume of the semen, but the fluid secreted does contain high levels of inorganic ions including calcium, chlorine, sodium, and magnesium. The prostate may become enlarged in older males and can interfere with urination. Sometimes referred to as Cowper's glands, the bulbourethral glands are paired glands located along the urethra near its exit from the pelvis. In bulls, fluid from these glands is secreted and expelled through the urethra prior to copulation and acts to flush out urine residue. These secretions in boars and stallions account for the gel-like portion of the semen which seals the cervix and prevents semen from flowing back into the vagina during natural service.

Penis

The penis is the male organ of copulation and deposits semen in the vagina or cervix (depending on the species) of the female. It can be divided into three general sections: 1) the glans, the free extremity which is well supplied with sensory nerves; 2) the body, the main portion; and 3) two crura (roots), which attach to the ischial arch of the pelvis. The glans varies from species to species. Bulls and rams have helmet-shaped glans. The glans of the boar is relatively small and corkscrew-shaped, allowing it to engage with the corkscrew-shaped cervix of the sow. The semen is deposited in the cervix of the sow instead of the vagina.

The penis may be one of two types: vascular or fibroelastic. Stallions have a vascular penis while the penis of bulls, rams, and boars are fibroelastic. The vascular penis enlarges by retaining blood in erectile tissue during periods of sexual excitement, causing an erection. The blood leaves the penis following ejaculation and thereby decreases the blood pressure and volume in the penis. Fibroelastic penises are firm when not erect, and only contain small amounts of erectile tissue. Therefore, a fibroelastic penis requires a very small amount of blood for erection and does not increase much in diameter. Bulls, rams, and boars have the ability to retract the penis completely into the body by the sigmoid flexure. The sigmoid flexure is an S-shaped bend in the penis that straightens during erection, lengthening the penis. On the other hand, stallions have a pair of smooth muscles which, when relaxed, allow the penis to be extended, and when contracted, draw the penis back in

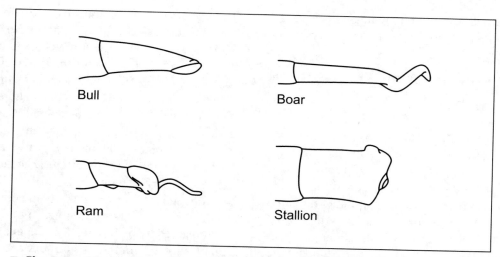

■ Fig. 5.7   Glans penis of the bull, boar, stallion, and ram. Note the corkscrew-shaped penis of the boar and the urethral process (filiform appendage) in the ram.

to the prepuce, an invaginated fold of skin that completely surrounds the free end of the penis.

Sterility

In both the male and female fetus, the gonads develop behind the kidneys. The ovaries in females remain in the same location but in the male, the testes descend from the site of origin down through the inguinal canals into the scrotum. The descent of the testes is usually complete by or shortly following birth. If there is a defect in development, one or both of the testes may fail to descend. This may occur in all species of farm animals, but is most common in stallions. If only one testis descends, the animal is referred to as a unilateral cryptorchid and may be fertile. If neither testis descends, the animal is called a bilateral cryptorchid and will likely be sterile. The sterility is due to the high temperature of the abdomen, which inhibits the production of sperm, but does not interfere with testosterone production. Since testosterone production is not affected, the animal will develop secondary sex characteristics and will otherwise appear to be normal. Cryptorchidism can be surgically corrected; however, because this condition can be inherited, it is not desirable to allow these animals to propagate, as it would allow for the perpetuation of the condition. Cryptorchids also develop testicular tumors at significantly higher

rates than normal males; therefore, castration is recommended.

Castration is the process of removing the testes. In livestock, this procedure prevents inferior quality males from reproducing. However, the primary purpose of castration is to influence the meat harvested from castrated males. Castration early in life prevents secondary sex characteristics from developing which improves the quality of the meat obtained at harvest. This process also ensures that meat from males will be absent of sex-related odor, especially in the case of swine. When non-surgical castration is performed, the spermatic cord is clamped to sever blood supply to the testes, or a band is placed around the neck of the scrotum to prevent blood supply to the testes. Both procedures result in regression of the testes. With surgical castration, the scrotum is opened and the testes are removed. In horses, castration generally improves the animal's performance and reduces fighting with other geldings. Without libido, males are generally much calmer and easier to handle. Castration should be done early in an animal's life to minimize stress. Sterile males can be produced by either vasectomy or epididectomy, which is the surgical removal of a section of either the vas deferens or the epididymis, respectively. This procedure does not affect the production of male hormones and the animal will still behave and appear as an intact male. Vasectomized males are sometimes used to aid in identifying females in estrus.

The Reproductive Process

Reproduction is an essential process required by all species for their continuation and propagation. There are three major purposes of reproduction: 1) perpetuation of the species, 2) genetic improvement, and 3) provision of food. Reproduction is the most economically important trait in farm animal production that determines the critical endpoints in production such as number of saleable animals, the number of replacement females or the number of eggs produced, and is essential to initiate lactation in milk producing species. For reproduction to occur, the animal must be anatomically sound and exhibit the physiological desire to mate (heat or estrus). Successful reproduction relies on coordination of the endocrine system and the reproductive system for the production of hormones required to accomplish germ cell production, fertilization, pregnancy, and parturition. This process is only active during certain phases of the animal's life and is generally age-dependent. Other factors affecting reproduction include photoperiod, the presence of the opposite gender, and the nutritional status of the animal.

Puberty
When an animal reaches a level of physiological maturity that permits conception, this is termed puberty.

Average Age and Weight at Puberty

	Age (mo)	Weight (kg)
Sow	4–7	68–90
Ewe	7–10	27–34
Mare	15–24	—
Dairy Cow	8–13	160–260
Beef Cow	10–15	225–310

On average, females will reach puberty when 45-55% of mature breed weight is attained; however, considerable variation within and between breeds has been documented and is influenced by factors including season and nutrition.

The signals that induce puberty vary among the different species, but two major influencing factors are age and weight. The age at which an animal reaches puberty is affected by both genetic makeup and environmental factors including nutrition, climate, and in some species, the proximity to a mature male. The weight at which an individual animal reaches puberty is determined by its genetic makeup, but the age at which this weight is attained is greatly influenced by nutritional plane during rearing. Evidence is emerging that suggest that even the nutrition of the mother will influence the time of puberty in her offspring.

In females, puberty is noted by the first estrus accompanied by ovulation. This depends on production of follicle stimulating hormone (FSH), luteinizing hormone (LH) and estrogen at circulating concentrations high enough to induce follicle growth, oocyte maturation, and ovulation. Phenotypically, puberty is characterized by the development of secondary sex characteristics that are generally associated with each sex. Common secondary sex characteristics in males include the hump on the necks of bulls and increased muscling. Characteristics in females include an increase in body fat and mammary development.

The Estrous Cycle
Following puberty, ovarian function will occur in a cyclical manner. This cycle is referred to as the estrous cycle and represents the period of time from one estrus to the next. The production of the female germ cells or ova is called oogenesis. Production of the ova is accomplished through the process of meiosis, resulting in a gamete (germ cell) containing half the number of chromosomes that are found in a somatic (body cell). Surrounding each ovum is a fluid-filled follicle that will begin to grow in size on the surface of the ovary as the time of estrus approaches. During this time, cells within the follicle are producing estrogens. The estrogen produced by this follicle is responsible for inducing estrous behavior. This follicle (or in polytocous animals, several follicles) will eventually rupture, thereby releasing the ovum (pl. ova) into the oviducts. The rupture of the follicle(s) and release of the oocyte(s) is referred to as ovulation. Ovulation will occur either during or near the end of estrus, or after estrus, depending upon the species. The two to five day period preceding estrus and ovulation is referred to as the follicular phase.

Following ovulation, the cells of the ruptured follicle wall will transform to become the corpus luteum (CL), representing the initiation of the luteal phase. During this transitional phase from a ruptured follicle to a CL, this structure is referred to as a corpus hemmorhagicum. The CL produces progesterone (the progestational hormone) during the luteal phase. The CL becomes fully functional during the five to seven days following ovulation and is a firm structure that protrudes from the surface of the ovary. The CL will be retained if the animal is pregnant and will continue to produce progesterone during gestation. The corpus luteum and the progesterone it produces are required for maintenance of pregnancy. If pregnancy does not occur, the CL will regress and progesterone concentrations will decrease. Regression of the corpus luteum occurs in response to prostaglandin $F_2\alpha$, a hormone secreted from the uterus when a viable conceptus is not present. The regression of the CL will lead to estrus in the next two to five days and the restarting of a new estrous cycle. When the CL regresses the only evidence of its existence is a very small white structure called the corpus albican. However, if there is a viable embryo in the uterus, regression of the CL is prevented by the embryo through a process termed maternal recognition of pregnancy. Proteins or hormones (depending upon the species) produced by embryos act to prevent production and/or release of prostaglandin $F_2\alpha$; leading to maintenance of the CL throughout gestation.

The sequence and timing of the events of the estrous cycle are controlled precisely by the hormonal interplay of the hypothalamic-pituitary-ovarian axis. The hypothalamus is a small region of the brain responsible for initiating the endocrine functions that control the estrous cycle. The hypothalamus releases gonadotropin-releasing hormone (GnRH), which is the first step in a cascade of hormonal events that coordinate ovarian function for reproductive success. Once released, GnRH acts on the anterior pituitary gland, which is located directly below the hypothalamus. In response to the GnRH, the anterior pituitary releases luteinizing hormone (LH) and follicle-stimulating hormone (FSH) into the blood stream. These hormones stimulate gonadal function and are therefore referred to as gonadotropins. In the female, FSH initiates the early growth of developing follicles. If adequate FSH is not present, smaller follicles will regress through a

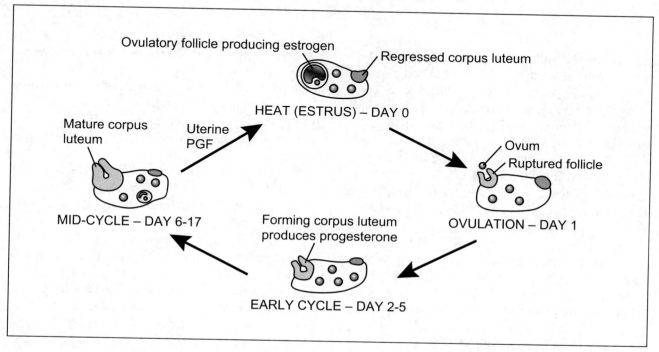

■ Fig. 5.8   Estrous cycle of cattle.

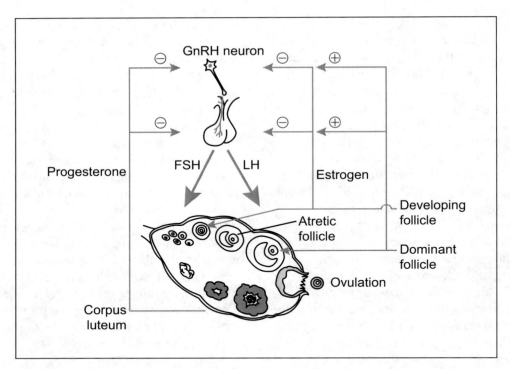

■ **Fig. 5.9** Successful reproduction involves the coordinated interactions of the hypothalamic-pituitary-ovarian axis. Estrogen released from the developing follicle is involved in negative feedback of GnRH secretion from the hypothalamus and FSH secretion from the anterior pituitary. This negative feedback is switched to positive feedback regulation when increased concentrations of estrogen produced by the preovulatory follicle initiates an LH surge, whereas progesterone is involved in negative feedback and inhibition of LH release.

process termed follicular atresia. Luteinizing hormone is critical for the final growth of follicles destined to ovulate (preovulatory follicles) and provides the final signal for ovulation via a massive release of LH termed the LH surge. Luteinizing hormone is also responsible for the transition of follicular cells to become luteal cells of the CL, through a process called luteinization. The release of GnRH from the hypothalamus occurs in a pulsatile manner; hence, the gonadotropins, and especially LH, are released in a pulsatile manner as well.

The secretion of LH and FSH is regulated by ovarian hormones that feed back on the hypothalamus to control GnRH secretion. Secretion of FSH is inhibited by estrogen, and another hormone called inhibin, that is produced by large ovarian follicles. When large follicles ovulate, or undergo atresia, a surge of FSH initiates growth of a new group of follicles. Progesterone inhibits LH secretion, therefore

when a CL is present, secretion of LH is low. When the CL regresses, and progesterone declines, the secretion of LH increases and causes the preovulatory follicle to develop. The high concentrations of estrogen produced by the preovulatory follicle acts at the hypothalamus to initiate the LH surge that causes ovulation.

The estrous cycle is described in four phases. Estrus is the first phase of the estrous cycle and represents the time during which the female is sexually receptive (day 0 of the cycle). High estrogen concentrations from the preovulatory follicle are responsible for sexual receptivity and for induction of the LH surge that initiates the process of ovulation. Estrus is followed by the second phase which is referred to as metestrus. This phase starts with ovulation on day 1, and continues through day 4 to 5 of the estrous cycle. In addition to ovulation, the other key event that occurs during this time is the forma-

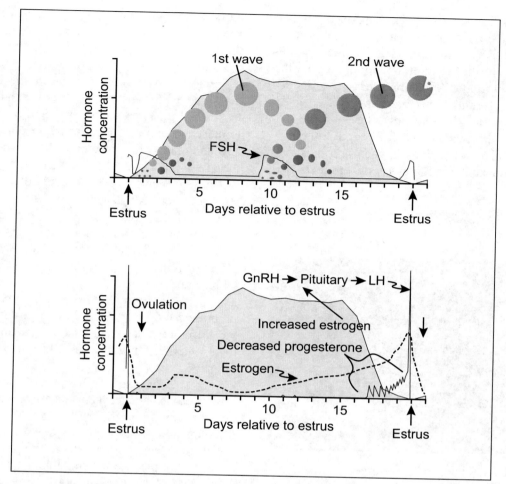

■ Fig. 5.10 Follicle stimulating hormone initiates early development of a follicle. In the absence of adequate FSH and LH, the follicle regresses and does not reach the ovulatory stage (top). As LH concentrations increase toward the end of the cycle due to decreasing progesterone, follicular development continues until peak estrogen concentrations initiate a surge in LH and ovulation (bottom).

tion of the CL and its increasing production of the hormone, progesterone. Diestrus (luteal phase) is the third phase of the estrous cycle and spans the period from approximately day 5 to day 17 in animals with a twenty-one day estrous cycle. During this period, the predominant hormone is progesterone that is being produced by the CL. If the female becomes pregnant, the CL will remain functional until parturition. If not pregnant, prostaglandin $F_2\alpha$ will cause luteal regression at the end of diestrus, leading to the final phase of the estrous cycle. The final phase is referred to as proestrus (follicular phase) and is typically two to five days in length. During this interval between regression of the CL and the next estrus, LH secretion is increasing, leading to increased growth of preovulatory follicles and the increasing production of estrogen to cause the next estrus.

Gestation

Gestation is the period of pregnancy for viviparous species that begins with fertilization of the ovum and ends with parturition. Fertilization results in the formation of the zygote, which will undergo cellular division to produce a 16-cell embryo referred to as a morula. Continuing development transforms the morula into a blastocyst, which moves from the oviduct into the uterus at this stage of development. As the embryo continues to develop, tissues further differentiate to form either the fetus or the placenta. Attachment to the uterus occurs via the placenta. This process, referred to as placentation, allows for exchanges between the maternal and fetal blood supply. It is through the placenta that the fetus receives oxygen and nutrients from the dam and eliminates waste products and

■ **Fig. 5.11** Females of some species will only show estrus on a regular interval during certain seasons of the year (seasonal breeders). The mare and most breeds of sheep and goats are seasonal breeders. Sheep and goats respond to decreasing daylength, therefore females of most breeds are most likely to become pregnant in the autumn as daylength shortens after the summer solstice, which is the longest day of the year in the northern hemisphere (June 21). The signal for increasing sexual activity is the hormone melatonin, which is secreted by the pineal gland. Secretion of melatonin increases in darkness, therefore as days get shorter, this hormone increases and stimulates the hypothalmic-pituitary-ovarian axis. On the other hand, mares are most likely to become pregnant in early spring. Their reproductive axis is stimulated by the progressive lengthening of days that occurs after the shortest day of the year on December 21 (winter solstice). Due to the length of gestation in horses and sheep, this seasonal pattern of reproduction helps ensure that parturition will occur in spring. (© ncn18, 2009. Under license from Shutterstock, Inc.)

carbon dioxide through the dam. In livestock species, there is no direct exchange of maternal and fetal blood, and the dam does not pass immunity to the fetus through the placenta.

Placental types differ between species and are classified by distribution of sites of exchange for nutrients and waste products between the fetal and maternal environments. In the diffuse placenta of the sow and mare, sites of exchange are distributed over the entire placenta. In the cotyledonary placenta of the cow and ewe exchange takes place at distinct structures termed placentomes, which are formed between button-like projections called caruncles from the endometrium and cotyledons of the placenta. In non-livestock species such as dogs, the placenta is described as a zonary placenta and is represented by a band of attachment. In primates exchange occurs with-in a disk shaped area of implantation and the placenta is termed discoidal. Due to the different placental structures in dogs and primates, there is immunity passed from the dam to the fetus.

The placenta is also a source of the hormones progesterone and estrogen. In early gestation, estrogen concentrations are low, but increase during middle and late gestation. Estrogens are produced by the placenta and work together with progesterone to develop and prepare the mammary glands for milk synthesis following parturition.

Parturition

Females preparing for birth often show behavioral changes such as the nesting behavior in which the female becomes more active; either building a nest or separating themselves from the herd. Prolactin is responsible for nesting behavior and also stimulates

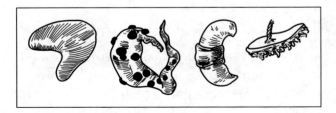

■ **Fig. 5.12** Comparative anatomy of placentation (left to right): diffuse placenta of the sow and mare, cotyledonary placenta of the cow and ewe, zonary placenta of the bitch, and discoidal placenta of primates.

milk synthesis. During this time, females generally will show discomfort and the mammary glands will become swollen as they fill with colostrum.

Parturition is the process of giving birth to offspring. The fetus initiates parturition by secreting the hormone cortisol approximately forty-eight hours prior to birth. Fetal cortisol triggers a variety of hormonal changes within the mother. High concentrations of progesterone that were present throughout pregnancy decline rapidly, while at the same time, estrogens, oxytocin, prostaglandins, prolactin, and relaxin all increase in concentration. The corpus luteum also regresses. Relaxin stimulates the pelvic muscles and ligaments to relax in preparation for the passage of the fetus through the birth canal. Oxytocin causes the gradually increasing uterine contractions required for birth.

There are three main stages in the process of parturition. The first stage includes the dilation of the cervix, which is caused by relaxin and estrogen. These hormones work to soften the cervix and stimulate the epithelial cells to secrete mucous. During this stage, uterine contractions move the fetus into the pelvic canal. During the second stage of parturition, the outer membrane of the placenta (allantochorionic sac) is expelled through the vulva, is typi-

cally ruptured in the process, and leads to the release of the fluids that surround the fetus during gestation. It is during this stage that the fetus will subsequently be expelled through the increasingly more intense uterine and abdominal contractions. During parturition, the umbilical cord becomes separated from the placenta thereby breaking the oxygen supply from the dam to the fetus. It is essential that parturition progresses rapidly after this time to ensure that the fetus/neonate receives adequate oxygen. The expulsion of the placenta represents the third and final stage of parturition. If the placenta is not passed, it is referred to as a retained placenta, and, in some species, is considered an emergency that requires immediate intervention.

Difficulty during parturition is referred to as dystocia. The most common cause of dystocia is that the fetus is too large to pass through the birth canal. Another common cause is that the fetus is presented in an abnormal birth position. Dystocia is more common with male fetuses as they are typically larger at birth than females. The normal birth position for most animals is front feet first, with the head between the front legs. In cases of dystocia, assistance is frequently required for the successful delivery of the fetus.

■ **Fig. 5.13**   Parturition is initiated by the pressure of the fetus against the cervix, which triggers a cascade of events that begin uterine contractions. In cows, mares, and ewes the position of the fetus is usually front feet first. In sows either tail or head-first presentation is often observed. (© Margo Harrison, 2009. Under license from Shutterstock, Inc.)

Reproductive Processes in Avians

Female Reproductive Anatomy

While the goal of reproduction in poultry is the same as that of mammalian species, the process is quite different. The major difference in poultry is that the species is oviparous. The development of young does not occur within the body, but instead eggs are fertilized and then laid outside of the body to continue their development. The eggs must be incubated either naturally by the female, or artificially until development is complete and the young are mature enough to hatch.

Unlike mammals, only the left ovary is functional in poultry. The right ovary regresses and the right oviduct atrophies, and therefore neither are involved in reproduction. A female chick hatches with approximately four thousand ova, each enclosed in separate follicles, attached to the left functional ovary. Maturation of these ova begins at puberty. The ova actually contain the yolks of the egg and are much larger than mammalian ova. Before each

Reproductive Characteristics of Females

	Estrous Cycle Length (days)	Estrous Duration	Ovulation	Gestation (days)
Sow	21	60 h	18–60 h	114
Ewe	16	30 h	1 h	150
Mare	21	4–10 d	24–48 h	336
Cow	21	14 h	10–14 h	280
Bitch	21	4–13 d	24–48 h	65
Queen	21	14–21 d	Induced	64

In the sow and bitch ovulation is relative to the onset of estrus, or receptivity of the female to the male. In the mare and ewe ovulation occurs prior to the end of estrus, whereas in the cow ovulation occurs after the end of estrus. In queens, release of ova is reliant on copulation.

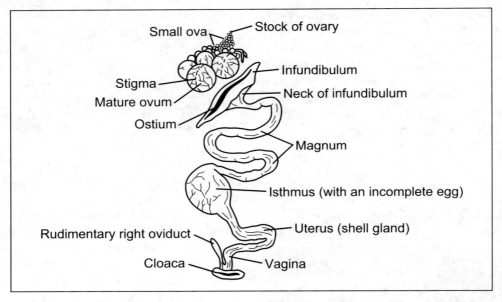

■ **Fig. 5.14** Reproductive anatomy of the hen.

ovum is ovulated, it grows as yellow and white yolk granules are deposited. The granules are high in nutrients, especially fat and protein as the yolk provides the source of nutrients for the developing embryo. This process is stimulated by FSH. Once the yolk has been fully formed, LH levels in the blood increase, stimulating ovulation along a line of the follicular wall termed stigma. The surge in LH that initiates ovulation relies on positive feed back of progesterone, this is in contrast to the stimulatory effects of estrogen on LH release in mammals. Furthermore, avians lack the formation of a corpus luteum. Following ovulation, the ovum is captured by the infindibulum and enters the oviduct. If sperm are present, fertilization will occur in the infindibulum. Sperm can remain viable for four to six days on average, depending on the species. However, the yolk (ovum) will only spend up to thirty minutes in the infindibulum and fertilization must occur within fifteen minutes. Whether the ovum is fertilized or

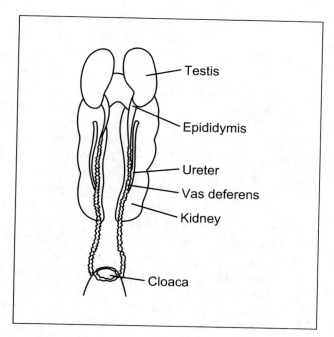

Testis

Epididymis

Ureter

Vas deferens

Kidney

Cloaca

■ **Fig. 5.15** Reproductive anatomy of the rooster.

not does not affect the remaining processes of egg formation.

The ovum moves from the infindibulum to the second section of the oviduct, the magnum, where it will stay for two to three hours. Here the thick portion of the albumen, the egg white, is deposited around the yolk. In the third part of the oviduct, the isthmus, two thin shell membranes are secreted and surround the albumen. These are the membranes that lie just inside the egg shell. The ovum also takes up water and mineral salts during its one and a half hour stay in the isthmus. The egg then moves into the uterus, which is sometimes referred to as the shell gland. The egg will spend eighteen to twenty-one hours in the uterus. Here, the rest of the albumen is added to the egg by diffusion. The egg also undergoes plumping, in which water and minerals diffuse through the membranes that were previously formed in the isthmus. Following plumping, calcification of the shell occurs and pigment is added. The eggshell is primarily composed of calcium carbonate ($CaCO_3$). There is no cervix present in the female reproductive system, though there is a sphincter muscle between the uterus and the vagina. Within the vagina, the cuticle or bloom is added, which is the very thin outer layer consisting primarily of protein. When the cuticle dries, it seals the

small pores present in the eggshell. The egg then passes through the vagina and into the cloaca and is expelled from the cloaca to the outside of the body. Oxytocin, a pituitary hormone, stimulates muscle contractions of the uterus, inducing laying of the egg. The cloaca is a common orifice for copulation, defecation, and expulsion of the egg.

The total time from ovulation to laying is about 25.5 hours on average in chickens, but varies with poultry species and is approximately forty-eight hours is ostriches. Poultry do not have an estrous cycle; instead, they are continual ovulators, laying eggs in succession once they reach sexual maturity. Approximately thirty minutes after an egg is laid, another one is ovulated. Eggs are usually laid in the morning, and are laid about thirty minutes later each day. Since birds are sensitive to photoperiod and laying of the egg becomes later each day, at some point the laying cycle will reset. The specific time pattern in which hens consecutively lay their eggs is called a clutch and is variable, ranging from one day to over two hundred days. Selection for egg production and improved management has resulted in birds that lay three hundred to three hundred and fifty days eggs consecutively, depending on species. In comparison, wild birds as well as emus and ostriches reproduce seasonally and tend to only lay eggs in the spring.

Male Reproductive Anatomy

The reproductive system of the male bird is much more simplistic than that of the mammalian species, consisting of two large testes; each with an epididymis and vas deferens that lead to a rudimentary phallus (penis) that is erectile in ducks and geese. The location of the testes differs from the reproductive system of the male mammals. The testes of the rooster are located high within the abdominal cavity, along the backbone, and near the front of the kidneys. As in mammals, sperm are produced and mature within the seminiferous tubules; however, spermatogenesis in birds occurs at core body temperature, on average 106.7° F, and is aided by the nightly cooling of the body to 104° F. The epididymis of the rooster is relatively small compared to mammals and has reduced capacity for sperm storage. Instead, the vas deferens, leading from the testicles to the cloaca, acts as the major storage site for sperm. Roosters lack accessory sex glands as well and as a consequence the volume of the seminal fluid is reduced. In poultry, the seminal fluid produced by the testicles, carries sperm from the testicles to two papillae present on the cloacal wall. These small, finger-like projections transfer sperm to a rudimentary phallus. During copulation, sperm is transferred from the male to the female through cloacal contact. This type of copulation is inefficient and unsuccessful in some species such as turkeys, therefore, artificial insemination is used in these species.

Reproductive Technology

Artificial Insemination

Artificial insemination (AI) is a procedure in which semen is collected from the male and placed into the female's uterus or cervix, using artificial means rather than copulation. Artificial insemination provides breeders and producers with opportunities to increase performance and profitability of their herds or flocks. Currently, AI is practiced in approximately 70% of dairy cattle, 90% of swine, less than 15% of beef cattle, and 95% of poultry. The use of AI is limited in sheep due to cervical anatomy and to some degree in horses as a result of stringent breed registry requirements or occlusions. There are three major advantages of AI including: 1) an increased rate of genetic improvement by use of superior sires, 2) the reduction or elimination of the cost and risk of owning and maintaining sires, and 3) the reduced risk of reproductive diseases. The process of AI requires the collection of semen from the male, the detection of estrus in the female, and the proper placement of semen in the female. Following good management practices, the reproductive efficiency using AI is comparable or improved compared to natural mating systems.

The most common method of semen collection is causing the male to ejaculate into an artificial vagina which has a collection receptacle. This is commonly referred to as the AV method. In this method of collection, a teaser-mount animal or a dummy mount is used. In cattle, cows, bulls, or steers can be used as teaser-mounts. As the bull mounts the teaser, the penis is guided into the artificial vagina and maintained until the bull dismounts. Alternatively, semen may be collected through the use of an electroejaculator. This method is typically used with males that are unable to mount a female

as a result of injury or age, or with males who are not trained to mount an animal or dummy for this purpose. An electrical prod is placed in the rectum of the male and an electrical current stimulates the accessory sex glands and contraction of muscles that causes ejaculation. The method of semen collection with boars is referred to as the gloved hand technique. Boars are usually trained to mount a dummy structure. Once the boar mounts, the tip of the penis is grasped firmly and pressure applied to simulate the cervix of the female until ejaculation is complete. A pre-warmed thermos is used to collect the semen. Semen is collected from poultry by using a stroking and milking technique. Stroking of the male bird from the pelvic arch to the pubic bones will cause the male to raise his tail and invert the cloaca. The enlarged portion of the vas deferens that stores semen, located near the entrance to the cloaca, is squeezed by the pressure of the thumb and forefinger and the semen is ejaculated.

Once semen is collected from the male, it is evaluated to determine concentration, motility and morphology. Since a single ejaculate of semen contains more sperm than needed to impregnate a female with AI, the semen is diluted with an extender solution containing nutrient, buffers, and antimicrobials and aliquoted into storage vials (straw). Aliqouted semen is either rapidly frozen in liquid nitrogen or cooled to prolong the life of the sperm. Semen from bulls can be frozen and stored indefinitely. On the other hand, semen of boars and stallions cannot be frozen efficiently; therefore, it must be kept fresh at 40° F. Poultry semen is usually used within two hours of collection.

One of the most important, yet difficult tasks in the process of artificial insemination is the detection of estrus in the female. The insertion of semen into the female must be coordinated with the ovulation to ensure fertilization of the ovum. Most species demonstrate specific behaviors that are characteristic of estrus, and aid in its detection. General behaviors demonstrated by females in estrus, regardless of the species, include restlessness, irritability, and excitability. If a male is present, females may exhibit increased vocalization and show interest in the male. Cows in estrus will spend more time than usual walking and spend less time resting or eating. They will mount other cows, and allow female or male cattle to mount her for a twelve to eighteen hour period, beginning twenty-four to twenty-eight hours before ovulation. When the cow shows standing heat (standing to be mounted by other cows) she is normally inseminated approximately twelve hours later. Sows in estrus will stand when pressure is applied to their back and will typically have a swollen, red vulva. Sows should be artificially inseminated each day they are in standing estrus. Ewes do not exhibit any obvious signs of estrus if a ram is not present, making detection rather difficult. In the presence of a ram, a ewe in estrus will roam around the ram and will rub his neck and body, while vigorously shaking her tail. Mares in estrus will allow the stallion to smell and bite at her. She will stand with her hind legs extended, lift her tail to the side, and lower her hindquarters. The clitoris will be exposed by frequent contractions (winking) of the labia. For accurate detection of estrus, the mare should be teased by a stallion. If the mare is aggressive toward the stallion, it is an indication that she is not in estrus, despite other signs being present. During estrus in the female dog, the lining of the uterus is sloughed and blood loss occurs. Cats in estrus will exhibit noticeable behavioral changes including increased affection and vocalization, and reduced appetite.

Estrous Synchronization

Estrus synchronization is a process in which estrus is induced in all the females in a herd or group at the same time, causing ovulation to occur simultaneously. This is done to help eliminate the problem of estrus detection. Estrus synchronization also simplifies the use of AI by having all or a select portion of the herd ready to be bred at the same time. Overall, synchronization reduces labor and allows for a more organized and efficient production system. It also may allow the producer to shift the parturition season to more closely coincide with the most favorable marketing patterns. There are several different approaches to synchronization in each species. These systems employ the use of prostaglandin $F_2\alpha$, GnRH and/or progestins (progesterone-like compounds) to control the estrous cycle.

Superovulation and Embryo Transfer

The process of embryo transfer involves the collection of fertilized embryos from one female to be placed in another female for further development. This technology became available in the livestock industry in the 1970's. Today it is most widely used in the cattle industry. The value of embryo transfer is the opportunity to produce more offspring from outstanding females, just as AI provides the opportunity to produce more offspring from superior males.

The first step of the process is to induce the female donating the embryos to superovulate. Cows generally only ovulate one ovum per cycle. Superovulation allows a superior cow to produce several ova for embryo transfer. This is accomplished by giving successive injections of FSH over three to four days to the cow to induce growth of multiple preovulatory follicles. Prostaglandin $F_2\alpha$ is injected causing the CL to regress and the cow will exhibit signs of estrus thirty-six to sixty hours following the injection. FSH prevents the death of follicles that would undergo atresia, allowing more follicles than usual to reach the preovulatory stage. The donor female is inseminated twelve hours following onset of estrus and again after another twelve hours to fertilize the ova. These resulting embryos are collected from the donor female seven days later through a process of flushing the uterus with fluid. The embryos are identified under a microscope and are examined for normal morphology. After being evaluated each embryo is frozen for storage and later use or placed immediately into a recipient female synchronized to be at the same stage of the

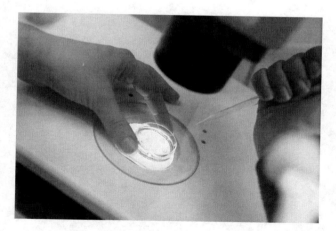

■ **Fig. 5.16**   Embryos produced by the donor female are collected and examined for normal morphology under a microscope before being frozen for storage or transferred to a recipient female. (© Monkey Business Images, 2009. Under license from Shutterstock, Inc.)

reproductive cycle as the donor female. The embryo, barring any complications, will develop into a fetus within the recipient. The offspring will carry the genetics of the sire and the donor female.

The most common method for transferring embryos to recipients is non-surgically, through a procedure very similar to that described for artificial insemination. The embryo is placed into an AI straw, the straw is placed in a transfer gun and carefully passed into the uterine horn that is adjacent to the ovary containing the functional CL. The pregnancy rates in cattle average 60% for commercial embryo transfer companies. Embryo transfer is typically limited to use with elite females. It is also mostly used in cattle. There is less incentive with swine since they are litter producers and have much shorter generation intervals. The procedure is difficult and costly to perform in sheep and goats.

In Vitro Fertilization

In vitro fertilization is the fertilization of ova outside of the body in a culture dish. The embryo is allowed to develop for approximately seven days in culture until it is transferred to a recipient. Oocytes can be collected from the ovary using a procedure referred to as ultrasound-guided follicular aspiration. These oocytes are then fertilized as described above. In vitro fertilization provides some advantages over other methods of embryo production. One advantage is that it allows for more frequent collections of ova as well as the collection of ova during pregnancy. Pregnancy rates with embryos produced in vitro are approaching those that can be achieved by traditional embryo transfer procedures. As technology advances, these rates will likely increase. On the downside, in vitro fertilization is not a perfected technology and it is rather time-consuming and expensive.

Lactation

"Man is the only creature that consumes without producing. He does not give milk, he does not lay eggs, he is too weak to pull the plough, he cannot run fast enough to catch rabbits. Yet he is lord of all the animals."

—*George Orwell (1903–1950)*

This chapter describes the process of lactation and the hormones involved in the control of milk production and letdown. You will gain an understanding of basic mammary anatomy and the anatomical difference of the mammary glands among various mammalian species. The lactation cycle and the processes involved in milk synthesis are emphasized. Current societal concerns, such as the use of the bovine somatotropin hormone, and industry concerns, including the incidence, detection, and treatment of mastitis, are discussed.

Lactation: A Historical Perspective

The origins of lactation trace to over two hundred million years ago, however, remain obscure. It was originally suggested that following the beginnings of live birth, prolonged contact between the mother and offspring may have been necessitated to maintain temperature of the young. Food originally brought to the young, a nutritional strategy maintained in the care of birds posthatch, may have gradually been replaced by maternal secretions derived from the mobilization of the female's body reserves. More recently, it was proposed that lactation evolved as a mechanism to maintain the moisture of eggs, but became an important alternative food source that led to the loss of egg yolk for nourishment and the rise of mammals. Regardless of origin, lactation is a universal feature of all mammals that affords continued

maternal contact between the female and her offspring that extends beyond the in-utero environment. Lactation enables the young to be born at a relatively immature stage and permits continued growth after birth. For many mammals, the developing fetus only represents a fraction of mature weight of the adult. The newborn of elephants, chimpanzees, and cattle are only 4–5% of maternal weight. Limiting the weight of the fetus in-utero allows the female to remain highly mobile during gestation. This ensure the animals ability to travel over long distances to secure food and flee predation when necessary. The prolonged investment in lactation and care of the young at the expense of the mother provides both nutritional support and protection through milk.

Overview of Lactation Strategies

A major characteristic of all mammals is that they employ lactation as a part of their reproductive strategy to feed and nourish their young. The complexity of the mammary system is coincident to the complexity of placentation and differs between monotremes, marsupials, and eutharians. In monotremes, which are egg laying mammals, primitive mammary glands are characterized by the absence of teats. For the duck-billed platypus, newly hatched immature young are reliant on milk for three to four months post hatch. On each side of the midline of the abdominal wall milk extrudes from one hundred to one hundred fifty paired tubal glands that open at the base of a stiff mammary hair. Secretory tubes have two cell layers, an inner secretory layer and an outer contractile layer. There is no internal storage of milk and as milk is produced it is secreted and subsequently licked by the young. In contrast, the mammary glands of the echidna are located in a pouch. As milk is produced, it is secreted

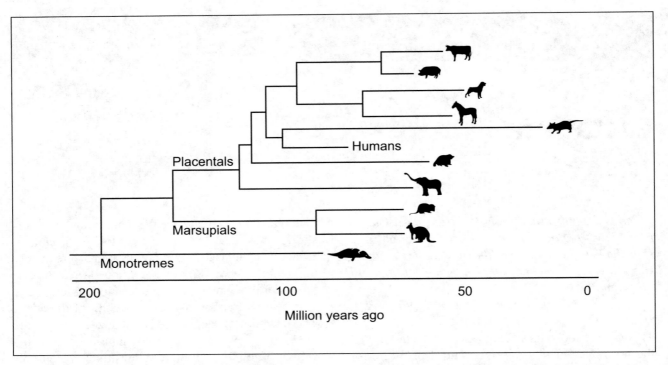

■ **Fig. 6.1** Lactation as a strategy to nourish the offspring evolved with the origins of mammals. It is evident in the egg bearing monotremes and remained with the divergence of placental mammals. (Animal images © Goran J, 2009. Under license from Shutterstock, Inc.)

from several ducts into depressions in the skin that collect the milk for consumption by the young.

Marsupials, including the koala bear, opossum, and kangaroo, give birth to live young after a relatively short gestation. The majority of the physiological development of the young occurs after birth and is coincident with an extensive lactation period relative to gestation. The placenta that develops is simple and only supports embryonic development for thirteen to forty days, depending on species. Generally referred to as pouched animals (although not all have a pouch), premature young that are characterized by limited neural, kidney, and lower limb development at birth will move from the uterus to a ventral pouch. For the kangaroo, within depressions of the pouch, teats are located and are associated with simple mammary glands. The development of the gland and teat corresponds to the suckling stimulus of the young. As the immature joey reaches the pouch it will seek out and latch on to a teat. As the joey suckles, the mammary gland will be stimulated to initiate lactation. The teat develops in size as the joey grows and the joey remains with the teat during the entire lactation. Once

the joey reaches a mature age to intermittently leave the pouch, it will return to suckle from the same teat. During this time, the female will conceive to support the development of another neonate. As the first joey leaves the pouch, the second is born, travels to the pouch, and begins to suckle from a different teat. Teats that are not stimulated by suckling will regress. Greater investment in lactation with minimal input into gestation allows the female to terminate the young under unfavorable conditions without reproductive costs, as there is little time invested into the gestation phase. For example, the female may eject the young from her pouch if there are not adequate resources to support lactation and postnatal growth; however, there will be limited delay in the time required to conceive a subsequent joey when resources become available. For the opossum, an excess of twenty-five young are born, however, only fifteen teats are available to nourish the young. Excess young are expendable and postnatal mortality rates are high, however maximal investment in lactation is ensured.

Placental mammals account for over 90% of all mammalian species and are distinguished by a com-

Fig. 6.2 Monotremes first appeared approximately 166.2 million years ago. A characteristic feature of these mammals is that they remain egg layers, but employ lactation to nourish the newly hatched young. (© clearviewstock, 2009. Under license from Shutterstock, Inc.)

Fig. 6.3 Marsupials first appeared approximately 144.7 million years ago. Although they are characterized by live birth, gestation is relatively short and the young are born extremely premature. The female's investment in the young is during the lactation phase. (© Tap10, 2009. Under license from Shutterstock, Inc.)

Mammary Gland Structure

The mammary glands of animals including goats, cattle, horses, and giraffes are located in the pelvic, or the inguinal region; whereas the mammary glands of the sow, dog, and cat develop in two parallel rows along the abdomen. Humans, other primates, and elephants have mammary glands located in the pectoral or breast region. The number of mammary glands varies among species, and in some species, the number of visible external glands differs from the number of internal glands that are present. Humans have two complex mammary glands, one in each breast, with each complex gland containing ten to twenty simple glands. Cows have four mammary glands, each with a corresponding teat. Ewes have similar anatomy to the cow, except there are only two mammary glands and two teats. Mares have two externally visible mammary glands, but they actually have four internal glands, serving each external gland with two streak canals, two teat cisterns, and two glands cisterns. The sow has two rows of mammary glands, each row usually having six or seven teats for a total of twelve to fourteen, although greater and lesser teat numbers have been reported. Each teat is served by two streak canals, two teat cisterns continuous with glands cisterns. The teats may

plex placenta. In contrast to marsupials, a greater investment is placed in gestation and the fetus develops in-utero, receiving maternal nutrients through the placenta. The young are classified as altricial or precocious depending on the maturity at birth. For example, altricial animals are considered immature at birth and are more reliant on maternal care than precocious neonates. Altricial young are incapable of coordinated movement, eyes are frequently closed, and are often born absent of hair and teeth. Mammals in this group include many rodent species. In contrast, precocious young, including many species of agricultural significance, are relatively mature at birth and senses of sight and hearing are fully developed. Precocial young are born with hair and teeth and often within minutes after birth, are capable of standing and fleeing from danger or predation. Although there is a greater investment in gestation, milk remains of vital importance for early nourishment and immune protection.

■ **Fig. 6.4**   Placental mammals first appeared approximately 101 million years ago. The young are classified as altricial (right) or precocious (left) according to maturity at birth. Extensive gestational development occurs relative to other mammals. In livestock species, lactation affords the newborn immunological protection against environmental pathogens until active immunity is established. (*Newborn mice:* © max blain, 2009. Under license from Shutterstock, Inc. *Newborn horse:* © Stephanie Coffman, 2009. Under license from Shutterstock, Inc.)

■ **Fig. 6.5**   Although predominantly considered a sex limited trait, occurring only in the female of a species, male lactation has been documented. In Dayaks, a species of Old World fruit bats, lactation occurs in both the male and female. While males produce only 15% of the volume of milk produced by females, they have well developed mammary tissue similar to that of lactating females. The significance in both sexes lactating is unknown. While some suggest male lactation is an artifact of a diet enriched in plant estrogens, others state that male lactation provides evidence of coordinated neonatal care of the young by both the female and male parent; however, it is unknown whether the young actually nurse from the male. (© Philip Date, 2009. Under license from Shutterstock, Inc.)

or may not be spatially paired; therefore the number on each side of the midline may differ.

External Structure

The mammary gland is commonly referred to as the udder in cattle, goats, and sheep. Each mammary gland is supplied by its own nervous and lymphatic systems and the right and left halves of the udder receive their own blood supply. There is no direct exchange of milk or blood between any of the glands; however, as blood recirculates throughout the body, it will pass through the other three mammary glands. Therefore, if one gland receives drug treatment, all milk produced must be discarded. If one mammary gland is injured; however, the remaining glands will continue to function since they are separate from one another.

In dairy cattle, the front mammary glands of the udder are smaller and produce and store approximately 40% of the milk, whereas the back two quarters are larger, producing and storing the remaining 60% of the milk. On average, a cow's udder will

■ **Fig. 6.6**   The gross anatomy of the mammary gland differs considerably across species. Whereas the cow has one mammary gland corresponding to each of four teats, sows have between twelve and fourteen teats each with two mammary glands associated. (*Left:* © Carsten Erler, 2009. Under license from Shutterstock, Inc. *Right:* © RestonImages, 2009. Under license from Shutterstock, Inc.)

hold twenty to forty pounds of milk, although some high producing cows may have udders holding up to sixty or seventy pounds of milk. In addition to milk weight, there is the weight of the blood present in the udder. For one gallon of milk to be produced, one hundred thirty gallons of blood must pass through the udder, thereby providing a continuous nutrient supply to the secretory cells. When considering both milk and blood, the udder holds a total of approximately one hundred pounds. It is important that the udder is well supported since it is located completely outside the body and is required to hold substantial weight.

The udder is supported by the suspensory system, consisting of a medial suspensory ligament and two lateral ligaments. The medial suspensory ligament provides the majority of support. This ligament is an elastic tissue that originates from the animal's midline and separates the two halves of the udder. The two lateral ligaments also provide support for the udder. These ligaments are non-elastic and fibrous. Originating about the udder, they are located on each side of the udder and meet with the medial ligament across the bottom of the udder.

Internal Structure

Alveoli are the primary functional units in the mammary gland responsible for milk synthesis and storage. Spherical and arranged in clusters within lobules, alveoli are lined with a single layer of epithelial (secretory) cells. As milk is synthesized, it is transferred to the lumen of alveoli and for some species, includ-

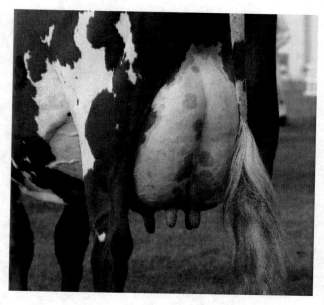

■ **Fig. 6.7**   The median suspensory ligament divides the udder into right and left halves and can be viewed from the rear of the cow. (© Chris Turner, 2009. Under license from Shutterstock, Inc.)

ing water buffalo and dairy cattle, the alveoli are the primary site of milk storage. The epithelial cells of alveoli have three major functions: 1) absorb nutrients and other precursors of milk from the bloodstream, 2) synthesize nutrients specific to milk, and 3) secrete milk components into the lumen of the alveolus. Each alveolus is vascularized for the delivery of nutrients and each is surrounded by specialized muscle cells termed myoepithelial cells. Contraction of the myoepithelial cells forces milk from the lumen of alveoli into a ductal network that transports milk to the gland cistern, which is continuous with the teat. For animals including dairy goats, the gland and teat cisterns are the primary site of milk storage. Milk exits from the teat cistern through the streak canal of the teat. At the junction of the teat cistern and streak canal is Fürstenberg's rosette, which contains bactericidal proteins and protects the mammary gland from infection.

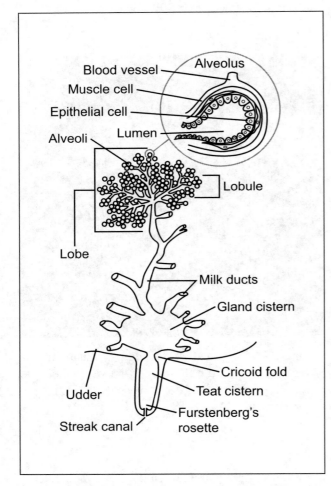

■ **Fig. 6.8** Milk synthesis occurs in the alveoli, which are comprised of a single layer of epithelial cells. Each alveolus is surrounded by myoepithelial cells. When the myoepithelial cells contract, milk is secreted into the lumen of the alveolus and subsequently into the milk ducts and then the gland cistern.

Further resistance to disease is provided by the teat sphincter that closes the canal when milk release is not occurring. The annular ring protects the mammary gland from foreign materials, most importantly from microbes, thereby minimizing exposure of the gland to infection. The canal also is lined with keratin, which has bacteriostatic properties.

Lactation Cycle

Mammals reproduce more than once, and therefore, lactate more than once. The mammary gland is one of a relatively few structures of the body that undergoes repeated cycles of structural development, functional differentiation, and regression. Structural development, or mammogenesis, begins the lactation cycle and is greatest during pregnancy. Functional differentiation represents active mammary tissues and is marked by lactogenesis, milk synthesis and secretion, and galactopoesis, or maintenance of lactation. Lactation is an event that coincides with the formation of colostrum, in coordination with parturition, and is maintained until the young no longer needs milk or milk is no longer removed from the gland. The mammary gland then undergoes regression, or involution, which is characterized by a return of the mammary gland to a non-lactating state.

Development and Growth of the Mammary Glands
In all mammals, the mammary gland is a highly evolved organ that arises from thickening of the epidermis during embryonic development. It consists of functional secretory tissue, also referred to as the parenchymal tissue, and a non-secretory framework known as the stroma. In the lactating mammary gland, the parenchymal tissue is composed of epithelial structures, such as alveoli and ducts, and the associated stroma consists of connective tissue as well as blood vessels. There also is considerable white adipose tissue that exists in a mammary gland from the early phases of fetal development extending through much of pregnancy.

The development of the mammary system is similar among lactating species and occurs during the prenatal, prepubertal, peripubertal, and postconception stages of development; however, the duration of each stage may differ. In cattle, the mammary gland begins formation at day twenty-five of embryonic development. A single layer of cells as-

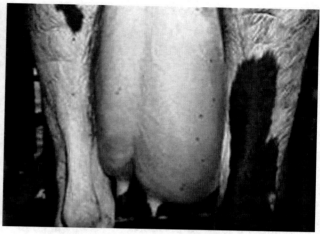

■ **Fig. 6.9** Following milk release, the teat sphincter will remain open for fifteen to sixty minutes, thus leaving the mammary gland open and susceptible to microbe entry during the hour following milking. A concern in lactating animals is mastitis, inflammation of the mammary gland that is most often caused by a bacterial infection. It occurs most often in dairy cattle, but it can affect all other domestic animals, especially swine, as well as humans. Symptoms of clinical mastitis include flakes or clots appearing in the milk (left) and the infected quarter of the udder is usually inflamed: swollen, red, hot and sensitive to the touch (right). A persistent low level of infection, referred to as subclinical infection, occurs more frequently in dairy herds than clinical infection, and significantly reduces both the production and quality of milk. Low level infections are generally not evident to the milker-operator, but can be detected using certain laboratory tests. The somatic cell count (SCC) is one such test that provides an indication of milk quality as well as the severity of subclinical mastitis. Mastitis must be treated with antibiotics. Milk from cows being treated for mastitis cannot be sold for human consumption due to zero tolerance laws that prevent milk that contains any antibiotic residues from being sold for human consumption. Therefore, mastitis leads to a decrease in profitability. If not treated promptly or appropriately, mastitis can cause cellular damage to the mammary gland, thereby causing a decrease in milk production and severe cases of mastitis can result in death. In efforts to control the incidence and severity of mastitis, milk producers often take some of the following precautions: ensuring proper cleaning and sanitation of the milking machines; using correct milking procedures that minimize the chance of infection; providing feed for the cows as they leave the parlor to encourage them to remain standing until their teat canals close; carefully monitoring somatic cell counts; and treating clinical cases promptly. (Courtesy of Joe Hogan, The Ohio State University)

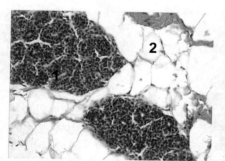
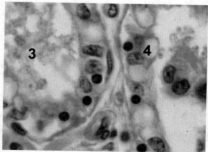
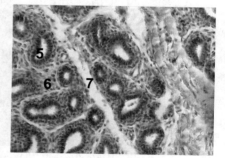

■ **Fig. 6.10** Haematoxylin and eosin stained bovine mammary tissue. Note the lobules (1) of the nonlactating developing mammary tissue and the presence of adipose tissue (2). Milk (3) is observed in the lumen of the alveoli in the lactating mammary tissue and lipid droplets are observed prior to being secreted from the epithelial cells (4). In the mammary gland undergoing involution, the alveoli (5) are reduced in size and there is considerable non-lactating stromal tissue (6) between alveoli. The excretory milk ducts also are observed (7). (Courtesy of Ann C. Ottobre, The Ohio State University)

sociates on each side of the midline to form the mammary streak. Along the mammary streak, distinct areas differentiate into mammary buds. In rodents, formation of the mammary buds occurs around embryonic day ten. The number and location of mammary bud formation determines the number and location of external mammary glands observed in the adult. Each bud will give rise to a primary spout, which is the precursor of the teat and gland cisterns that are evident by day ninety of gestation in cattle. Several secondary sprouts will arise from each primary sprout. These secondary sprouts represent future mammary ducts and will become canalized shortly before birth. Additional events in prenatal mammary development include the formation of the mammary fat pad. First observed at day eighty of gestation in cattle and day sixteen of the rodent, the mammary fat pad supports late fetal and postnatal ductal development. By six months of gestation the mammary tissue of the bovine fetus is well developed and further structural development does not occur. Immediately after birth, the immature ductal system will regress while the mammary gland experiences isometric growth, in which the rate of growth parallels that of the body. Prior to the onset of puberty, the isometric growth of the mammary gland is replaced by allometric growth, in which the rate of growth exceeds that of the body. Signaled by ovarian function and estrogen production, allometric growth corresponds to proliferation and expansion of the ductal system. Interestingly, excess energy intake during the period of allometric growth can impair mammary development and reduce milk production during the subsequent lactation in dairy cattle. The allometric growth ceases with subsequent estrous cycles, however, fluctuations in estrogen and progesterone that occur during the estrous cycle are important toward complete ductal development and establishment of the lobule-alveolar system.

The postconception stage of mammary development is characterized by increased progesterone concentrations and extensive lobule-alveolar development. Although alveolus budding occurs prior to conception, it is not until pregnancy that the secretory cells develop. There is a significant increase in the number of cells, and thus the amount of DNA, of mammary tissue during pregnancy with the greatest increases corresponding to the last stages of gestation when rapid fetal development also occurs.

Gestation also corresponds to increased vascularization of the mammary gland. Structural development of the mammary gland during gestation requires both estrogen and progesterone.

Milk Synthesis and Secretion

The increase in size of the mammary gland just prior to parturition is due to the accumulation of milk in the alveoli. As parturition approaches, prolactin from the anterior pituitary initiates and maintains lactation. During parturition prolactin and oxytocin, in addition to other hormones, peak to stimulate the mammary glands to come into a full lactational state. This allows for the production of colostrum for the first few days, and then provides an increasing amount of milk for subsequent days. It is not until several weeks following parturition that milk production will reach its peak. The reason for this delay in maximum output is not fully known, but may be attributed to the many physiological and biochemical changes that the mammary gland must undergo. On average, dairy cattle achieve maximal milk production between fifty and seventy days postcalving and may produce in excess of one hundred pounds of milk per day during peak lactation. In contrast, dairy goats achieve peak milk production between thirty and forty-five days postkidding and produce an average of 9.4 pounds of milk per day during peak lactation. Once peak production has been reached, milk production will begin to decline as the secretory cells lose their functional abilities. The prolonged and steady production following the peak is referred to as persistency. Persistency is necessary for high production rates over the entire lactation period. Many factors may affect persistency including genetics, nutrition, disease, as well as the frequency and completeness of milking.

Oxytocin is the most notable hormone responsible for stimulating milk letdown (release). Produced in the hypothalamus and released from the posterior pituitary gland, oxytocin reaches the mammary gland via the bloodstream. At the mammary gland, oxytocin acts on myoepithelial cells, causing them to contract. As stated, these cells surround the secretory cells and the contraction of these myoepithelial cells forces the milk that is stored in the lumen into the ducts that lead towards the gland and test cisterns. The initiation of milk letdown increases the pressure in the mammary gland, thereby promoting milk letdown. In dairy cattle, one to two minutes following the initial stimulation of the udder, oxytocin and mammary pressures are the greatest. Six to seven minutes following initial stimulation, the liver and kidney remove the oxytocin from the bloodstream, causing milk letdown to cease.

Oxytocin release is dependent on the female recognizing a stimulus. Usually, milk letdown is initiated by stimulation of the teats by her offspring beginning to nurse. Females also are conditioned to release milk by other stimuli associated with milk removal, such as the visual appearance of the offspring; or in the case of dairy animals, the sights and sounds associated with the milking parlor.

Epinephrine (adrenaline) and norepinephrine are hormones that also play a role in lactation; however, they work in opposition to oxytocin. These hormones are released when an animal becomes stressed, frightened, or nervous. Epinephrine and norepinephrine inhibit milk letdown by causing the blood that usually bathes the myoepithelial fibers and contains oxytocin, to be shunted to the body's extremities. Milk letdown will thereby decrease as the fibers relax due to the lack of oxytocin. During stress, the hypothalamus may fail to stimulate adequate release of oxytocin from the posterior pituitary or the myoepithelial cells may fail to respond to the oxytocin. Due to these effects, it is important to minimize stress on animals during milking time so as to not interfere with milk letdown.

Involution

During this period following peak production, the mammary gland will undergo a gradual involution in which it will return to its normal state and size; decreasing in weight, volume, and productivity. Involution may involve a reduction in alveoli size and their synthetic capacity, as occurs in dairy cattle; or extensive tissue degeneration and an almost complete loss of alveoli, which has been observed in mice. The loss of the epithelial cells of alveoli that occurs in rodents is considered programmed cell death, or apoptosis. Once the female becomes pregnant again, structural development of the mammary tissue is once again initiated. Redevelopment of the alveolar system will support the ensuing lactation. The increase and decrease in milk production during lactation is referred to as the lactation curve. The lactation curve is a plot of milk production over the duration of the lactation period and each species has a characteristic lactation curve. Involution and the

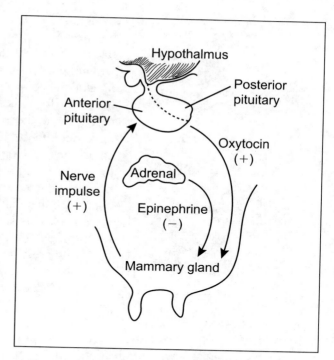

■ **Fig. 6.11** Milk ejection is stimulated by oxytocin release from the anterior pituitary. Direct stimulation of the teats by the milker's hands or suckling by the young can initiate a nerve impulse to trigger oxytocin release. In addition, cows associate the milking routine with certain environmental cues and will begin to eject milk in response to these cues, which may include the sounds of the milking equipment or the presence of feed. It is important to minimize stress as the release of epinephrine by the adrenal glands works in opposition to oxytocin to inhibit milk ejection.

gradual decline in milk production demonstrated over the lactation curve are inevitable and occur despite continued milk removal from the mammary glands. Cessation of milk removal, however, will initiate involution at any point along the lactation curve and promote the return of the mammary gland to a non-lactating state.

Milk Composition

Milk is the primary source of nutrition for mammalian infants during early postnatal life and is

Fig. 6.12   A naturally produced growth hormone, also known as bovine somatotropin (BST), increases milk production by decreasing the rate of decline in milk production following peak lactation; however, it will not prevent involution or eliminate cessation of lactation. The mode of action is not fully known, either an increase in enzymatic activity necessary for milk production, an increase in the availability of nutrient precursors to the cells, or a combination of both contribute to increased milk yield. In the 1980's, following years of research, pharmaceutical companies developed a recombinant bovine somatotropin (rBST) product that could be injected into cows to complement their natural concentrations of somatotropin. Both the FDA and National Institute of Health concluded that dairy products produced from the milk of cows treated with rBST were safe for human consumption. In 1993, based on the results of numerous studies, the FDA approved the use of BST. In 2009, following pressure from consumers who demanded milk products free of artificial growth hormones, rBST use diminished in the dairy industry.
(© Jaimie Duplass, 2009. Under license from Shutterstock, Inc.)

comprised of water, triglycerides, lactose, protein, minerals, and vitamins. Milk production in most females corresponds to the nutrient needs of the young. For example, the milk of marine mammals that occupy cold environments is greater in lipid and negligible in lactose as these young do not readily digest carbohydrates, yet deposit considerable lipid after birth for insulation. In addition, most females produce only enough milk to feed their young, however, dairy animals have been bred and developed to maximize milk production so excess is available for human consumption.

Milk synthesis occurs in the alveoli, where epithelial cells receive a continuous supply of nutrients from the blood. The epithelial cells of the alveoli acquire glucose, medium and short chain fatty acids, vitamins, and minerals from the circulation. In addition, milk specific nutrients including lactose and casein are synthesized locally.

Carbohydrates

The primary carbohydrate found in the milk of nearly all species is lactose. Only the epithelial or secretory cells produce lactose, which is a disaccha-

Milk Composition

	Water (%)	Lactose (%)	Fat (%)	Protein (%)	Energy (kcal/100g)
Cow	87	4.6	3.9	3.2	74
Human	87	7.1	4.5	0.9	72
Buffalo	83	4.8	7.4	3.8	101
Goat	87	4.3	4.5	3.2	70
Donkey	88	7.4	1.4	2	44
Elephant	78	4.7	11.6	5	143
Rat	79	2.6	10.3	8.4	137
Bat	60	3.4	18	12.1	223
Seal	35	0.1	53	9	516

■ **Fig. 6.13**   There is a greater than two fold increase in blood flow to the mammary glands prior to parturition. It is estimated that each liter of milk requires the circulation of five hundred liters of blood through the mammary glands. The abdominal vein, otherwise known as the milk vein, is highly visible under the skin of the lactating cow. (© Luca Flor, 2009. Under license from Shutterstock, Inc.)

ride of glucose and galactose. All glucose required by the mammary tissue is provided by the bloodstream, as the mammary gland is incapable of synthesizing glucose. The glucose may be used directly by the epithelial cells for energy, converted to glycerol for triglyceride synthesis, or converted to galactose and used for the production of lactose. The inability to synthesize glucose makes glucose availability an important limiting factor in milk component synthesis. A reduction in circulating glucose limits the amount of lactose synthesized by mammary tissue. Furthermore, lactose production contributes to milk volume. Lactose secretion into the lumen of the alveoli increases the concentrations of dissolved solutes relative to the bloodstream. As this occurs, water is drawn into the lumen of the alveoli to maintain osmotic pressure. This results in a high concentration of water in milk, generally greater than 80% in most species. As lactose production declines, the amount of milk produced per day also declines.

Since lactose is a disaccharide, it must be broken down in the small intestine following consumption by the enzyme lactase. Some individuals lack adequate amounts of lactase and are therefore un-

able to degrade lactose. This lack of lactase results in a condition referred to as lactose intolerance. Individuals with this condition experience gastrointestinal distress, including diarrhea, intestinal gas, and bloating following milk consumption. The incidence of lactose intolerance varies widely with approximately 90% of the population of Asian ancestry affected, 70% of the African-American population, and only 2–8% of those of Scandinavian and Western European descent affected. Individuals with lactose intolerance can alleviate the condition by consuming lactose free products or consuming cultured products that have undergone fermentation of the lactose.

Lactose intolerance is frequently misperceived as a milk allergy since the two conditions share many symptoms. Milk allergy experienced by humans is in response to proteins found in milk. The direct protein responsible for the allergenic response remains unknown and both casein and B-lactoglobulin are suspected milk allergens. The incidence of milk protein allergy in human infants is estimated to be less than 1%.

Protein

There are many proteins found in milk, though the primary protein is casein, comprising over 80% of the total milk protein. The mammary gland is the only tissue capable of synthesizing casein. There are many forms of casein and all carry negative charges as a result of the phosphate groups held in associations with the proteins. The epithelial cells sequester calcium from the bloodstream in order to secrete these negatively charged proteins, making casein responsible for the calcium content of milk. Milk serum proteins make up approximately 18% of the protein in milk. These milk serum proteins provide amino acids for the synthesis of other proteins by the body when digested.

Colostrum, the first milk produced following parturition, contains increased concentrations of proteins, as well as fat, minerals, and vitamins A and C. The increased protein is due to the transfer of immunoglobulins (antibodies) into the milk. These immunoglobulins provide the offspring with increased resistance to diseases and infections. This type of immunity is referred to as passive immunity since the animal receives the antibodies from the mother's milk. The functionality of these immunoglobins depends on their absorption from the small intestine.

Fig. 6.14 Calcium required to neutralize the protein casein is removed from the bloodstream of the female. In early lactation, the demand for calcium in milk production and the removal of calcium from the blood can cause a rapid decline in circulating calcium that exceeds the ability to mobilize calcium from body reserves. As a consequence, hypocalcemia may occur and in dairy cattle, the reduced blood calcium may result in milk fever, which is characterized by muscle weakness, loss of appetite, and eventual heart failure if left unattended. This condition, also referred to as parturient paresis, is treatable by an intravenous dose of calcium. (© John Czenke, 2009. Under license from Shutterstock, Inc.)

Mammals may be classified by the mechanism of acquired immunity. For pigs, horses, goats, and cattle, immunity is acquired passively through the consumption of colostrum. For dogs, rats, mice, and hamsters, transfer of antibodies to the young occurs both in-utero through placental transport and postnatal through colostrum. In the last classification, which includes humans and rabbits, placental transfer of antibodies is the only source for passive immunity. The intestine is able to absorb large macromolecules such as immunoglobulins as a consequence of its immaturity. Immunoglobulins absorb to the surface of the enterocyte and are internalized by pinocytosis. The absorbed immunoglobulins are subsequently transported into the bloodstream. As the intestine matures, it is no longer able to absorb immunoglobulins, a process known as gut closure. Gut closure occurs at twenty-four hours in the calf, thirty-six to forty-eight hours in the pig, twenty-four to forty-eight hours in the foal, and twenty-four to forty-eight hours in the dog and cat; therefore, it is essential that the offspring receive colostrum as soon as possible following birth. Studies in pigs show that the time of gut closure can be extended if the neonate is fasted or fails to suckle immediately following birth, increasing the likelihood of receiving passive immunity. The production of colostrum by the female exceeds the window of gut closure in the neonate as colostrum is produced during the initial three to four days postpartum; however the quality of colostrum decreases during this transition. The most important antibody in the colostrum is IgG, which acts as a nonspecific antibody.

Lipids

Over 90% of the lipids found in milk are triglycerides, while the remaining 10% are cholesterol and phospholipids. Triglycerides of varying chain length and saturation are found in milk. The sources of milk lipids are: 1) circulation, originating from diet or mobilization of body fat, and 2) production by the mammary tissue. The characteristics of milk fat depend on the source of the fatty acids. Long chain fatty acids in milk are absorbed from the bloodstream, while short and medium chained fatty acids are synthesized by the mammary tissue.

The majority of dietary unsaturated fatty acids in ruminant species are saturated by the microorganisms present in the rumen. By the time the fats reach the small intestine and are absorbed, they are predominantly saturated; however, lesser amounts of unsaturated fatty acids are absorbed and incorporated into milk as well. Mammary tissue synthesis of fatty acids involves glucose as the primary precursor for fatty acid synthesis in the mammary gland of nonruminants, whereas the volatile fatty acid acetate is the primary precursor for fatty acid synthesis in ruminants, in light of the fact that ruminant species have very limited supplies of glucose. Since the amount of milk fat depends on the amount of acetate produced, and the amount of acetate present depends on the amount of fiber in the diet, the amount of fat in milk can be manipulated to some extent by altering the animal's diet.

Dairy Cattle

"All the good ideas I ever had came to me when I was milking a cow."

—*Grant Wood, (1891–1942)*

This chapter introduces the different breeds of dairy cattle and their specific contributions to the United States dairy industry. The role and size of the dairy industry is highlighted along with the basic management of dairy farms, facilities associated with dairy farming, and diseases of the dairy industry. In addition, the importance of dairy as a dietary component and the nutritional benefits of milk are explained.

Dairy Cattle: A Historical Perspective

The use of cow's milk for human consumption first occurred in northeast Africa and Asia. Early evidence of dairying can be traced through the written records of the Sumerians of Mesopotamia dating to 6000 B.C. In the Euphrates Valley ancient architectural art depicts cows being milked from behind; however, around 3000 B.C. Egyptian records indicate that cows were milked from the side. In both cultures, calves were placed in front of the cows during milking, which would stimulate milk release in the dam. Records of dairying in Greece date to 1550 B.C. and in Rome, 750 B.C. Milk was an important constituent of the diet; however, lack of refrigeration meant that consumption of milk was primarily by shepherds and farmers, who consumed milk fresh after milking the cow, and the wealthy who could pay to have the fresh milk expressly delivered. Sources of animal milk varied through out the world, as it does today; however, cattle represent the primary species milked today and contribute over 80% of milk consumed worldwide. The first recognition of the benefits of dairy products can be traced to Aristotle. In Aristotle's (384–322 B.C.) writings on the history of animals he documented that the cow was a mammal producing milk in excess of what was required by the calf and could be used to benefit man in processes including tooth development.

In the United States specialized breeds of cattle for dairying did not exist until the 1850s. Although the first cows to provide milk arrived in Jamestown in 1611, these cows were the same animals that supplied labor and meat. Usually, one cow was sufficient for the family and no surplus of milk was produced for sale. Milk was immediately consumed due to its tendency to spoil. However, technological advances following the Civil War allowed for the preservation of excess milk, providing the foundation of today's current dairy industry. The development of condensed milk, mechanical refrigeration, and the process of pasteurization (controlled heating to destroy microorganisms) helped to expedite the development of the industry. Soon, large dairy herds were established by importing significant numbers of cows from Europe to sustain the growing industry. The breeds of imported cows varied and breed associations were formed to track each breed's registry.

There have been many milestones that have marked the advancements in the dairy industry. In 1776 the first ice cream parlor opened and during the years of 1848 to 1873, sixty-nine patents were filed for hand crank ice cream freezers. The 1800s also marked the first cheese factory (1851), a centrifugal cream separator (1878), and the invention of the milk bottle (1884). The Babcock Cream Test developed in 1890 served as the basis for setting milk prices by determining the amount of milk fat contained within the milk. Commercial pasteurization soon followed in 1895 and homogenization in 1919. The first milking machines were developed as early

■ **Fig. 7.1**   The Egyptian goddess of love, Hathor, is often depicted as a heavenly cow. (© Bill McKelvie, 2009. Under license from Shutterstock, Inc.)

as 1903 and in the 1930s, dairy farms began to utilize bulk tanks in replacement of the milk can. The number of dairy cows reached its peak in 1945; however, peak milk production was not reached until 1964, which is the same year that the plastic milk container was introduced. In the 1970s nutritional labeling of milk became common and by the late 1980s, the sales of reduced fat and skim milk exceeded whole milk sales. The demands of the consumer for dairy products have been met by a reduction in dairy cows and increased milk production per cow during the last century. In the last decade the demand for organic milk has influenced the dairy industry. The number of certified organic dairy cows tripled between 1992 and 1994 and doubled between 1994 and 1997 and again during 1997 and 2002. Although sales of organic milk accounted for only 2.7% of total milk sales in 2007, the demand by consumer continues to increase steadily.

Breeds of Dairy Cattle

Cattle that are considered dairy breeds are those that excel in their ability to produce excess quantities of milk for a sustained period of time. Today, dairy cattle can be found in every state in America and consist primarily of the five specialized dairy breeds that were imported to the United States before or during the 1860s. These breeds are still in use today and include the Ayrshire, Guernsey, Holstein, Jersey, and Brown Swiss. The Milking Shorthorn once considered a dual purpose breed as it was once used for both milk and beef production is an additional dairy breed that exists in the USA..

The Holstein-Friesian originated from the Netherlands and Northern Germany. Its origins trace to black and white cattle owned by Batavian and Friesian immigrants to the region. Interbreeding of the cattle contributed to the characteristic black and white markings of today's breed. The breed's first importations to the United States occurred in the mid 1600s by Dutch sailors. However, significant importation did not occur until the 1860s and present-day Holsteins are descendents of the cattle imported from 1877 to 1905, after which time importations stopped. In the United States the breed is commonly called Holstein; elsewhere, it is known as Friesian.

The Holstein displays either a dominant black and white spotted pattern, or less common, a recessive red and white pattern. For registration, the tail and underside should contain white coloring and no

■ **Fig. 7.2** Holstein (© Viorel Sima, 2009. Under license from Shutterstock, Inc.)

black points should touch the hoofs. Solid black and solid white animals are unable to be registered with the breed. Holsteins are the largest of the dairy cattle breeds. They are characterized by large udders, and increased milk production relative to the other breeds. Holsteins are ranked first among dairy breeds in average milk production and can produce more than one hundred pounds of milk per day during peak lactation. In 2007, average milk production rates of 22,946 pounds per year were reported. Increased production capacity contributes to the Holsteins susceptibility to udder problems due to the high stress placed on the udder ligaments. Holsteins rank fifth in milk fat production, with an average milk fat of 3.5 percent. The Holstein is the major dairy breed by far in the United States, accounting for almost 95% of all dairy cows. An estimated nineteen million animals are currently registered by the Holstein Association and represent 20% of the Holstein population in the United States.

The Jersey originated from the Island of Jersey, located between the coasts of France and England and is considered one of the oldest purebred breeds of dairy cattle, due in part to its isolation by the island. Importation first occurred around 1815, with major importations occurring between 1870 and 1890. Jerseys can range in shades of cream, to light fawn, to nearly black. All Jerseys have darkly pigmented skin and black muzzles. They are the smallest of the dairy breeds and are noted for their large eyes. This breed has well attached udders and is known for its efficient use of feed and excellent

grazing abilities. The breed also has a productive life span that exceeds the average of all other dairy breeds by 185 days. Jerseys rank fourth in average milk production with an average yield of 16,539 pounds of milk per year; however, this breed is first in its production of milk fat with a percentage of 4.7. Additionally, milk from Jersey cows yields 20% more cheese and 30% more butter relative to market-average milk. The Jersey is the second most popular dairy breed in the United States; however, the breed constitutes less than 5% of all dairy cattle and current registrations are estimated at 440,000.

The Brown Swiss originated from the Alps of Switzerland. Importations first occurred in 1869 and the Brown Swiss cattle of today are descendants from twenty-five imported bulls and one hundred forty imported cows. Brown Swiss vary in solid shades of brown, ranging from light to dark. The nose and tongue of the Brown Swiss are characteristically black with a light colored band around the muzzle. The early breed was strong and had a tendency to be heavy muscled, which lead to their earlier classification as a dual purpose breed. Today, the breed has retained its large frame, but is more refined for the dairy industry. Heifers of this breed mature more slowly than those of some other dairy breeds and are noted for heat tolerance. Brown Swiss rank second in average milk production with annual production rates of 21,242 pounds of milk. The breed ranks third in milk fat production, producing an average of 4.1 percent milk fat and is a desired breed for cheese production due to the protein content and the fat to protein ratio

■ **Fig. 7.3** Jersey (Courtesy American Jersey Cattle Association)

of the milk. The Brown Swiss is third in registration numbers with an estimated 10,076 registries.

The Guernsey breed originated on the Island of Guernsey, located in the English Channel between France and England. The breed was developed by Monks through the careful selection of desired traits. Guernsey's were first imported into the United States in 1840; however, major importation did not occur until after 1870. It is estimated that over thirteen thousand head of Guernsey cattle were brought into the United States. The breed may be any shade of fawn and contain clearly defined white markings. The skin of Guernsey is yellow in color compared to the darkly pigmented skin of the Jersey. The Guernsey is an early maturing breed

■ **Fig. 7.4** Brown Swiss (© nagib, 2009. Under license from Shutterstock, Inc.)

noted for producing milk typically yellow in color and with a high milk fat content of 4.5%. The yellow color is a result of increased concentrations of β-carotene in the milk. The breed ranks second among the dairy breeds in average milk fat and fifth in average milk production with an annual yield of 15,877 pounds. Milk production is sustained by consuming 20% to 30% less feed per pound of milk produced compared to larger breeds of dairy cattle. The Guernsey is the fourth most popular dairy breed in the United States.

The Ayrshire has its origins in Ayrshire County in Southwestern Scotland. The first importation of Ayrshires into the United States occurred in 1822. Ayrshires may be solid white or light to deep brown with white coloring. The preferred coloring is a distinctive red and white. The breed is noted for its symmetrical and well attached udders, sturdy legs and feet, and excellent grazing ability. The vigor of the offspring and their ease of care, contribute to the desirability of the Ayrshire breed. Ayrshires rank third among the dairy breeds in milk production and average 17,230 pounds of milk per cow annually. The breed ranks fourth among the five dairy breeds in milk fat production, with an average of 3.8% milk fat. Ayrshires are currently ranked fifth in United States dairy registrations.

The Shorthorn was developed in England and first served as a triple purpose breed supplying meat, milk, and draft power to early settlers of the United States in 1783. However, through careful selection, the breed was adapted for either milk or meat production and in 1882 a breed association was established to distinguish both types of

■ **Fig. 7.5** Guernsey (© Marcel Jancovic, 2009. Under license from Shutterstock, Inc.)

Shorthorn cattle. Although it still maintains a status of a dual purpose breed, Milking Shorthorns were recognized as a distinct dairy breed in 1969. Milking Shorthorns can be red, white, or a combination of the two. This breed is known for its adaptability and continues to undergo more refinement in the United States to improve its milk producing ability. The breed averages 15,000 pounds of milk annually with an average milk fat content of 3.3%. The Milking Shorthorn is sixth in United States dairy breeds registrations.

United States Dairy Industry

Dairy cattle are found in each of the fifty states. Early dairying relied on dairy farms to be in close proximity to areas of large human populations due to the perishable nature of milk. Today, dairy farms are concentrated in the North and West, with Western areas offering the advantage of reduced costs of production relative to other regions of the United States. Production has shifted to these states to accommodate an increasing human population. The ten largest milk producing states include: California, Wisconsin, New York, Idaho, Pennsylvania, Minnesota, Texas, New Mexico, Michigan, and Washington. While many of these states also are densely populated, the exceptions are Wisconsin and Idaho. Both of these states produce much more milk than their population requires. Idaho's proximity to West Coast states allows excess product to be shipped to this location, whereas, Wisconsin has historically maintained a strong milk production industry and utilizes its many dairy farms

■ **Fig. 7.6** Ayrshire (© Viorel Sima, 2009. Under license from Shutterstock, Inc.)

Breed Characteristics

Breed	Body Weight (lb)	Milk (lb/305 d)	Fat (%)	Protein (%)	Lactose (%)	Solids (%)
Ayrshire	1200	17,230	3.88	3.17	4.60	12.77
Brown Swiss	1400	21,242	4.10	3.32	4.68	13.08
Guernsey	1300	15,877	4.50	3.37	4.71	14.04
Holstein	1400	22,946	3.50	3.06	4.68	12.16
Jersey	1000	16,539	4.68	3.63	4.83	14.42
Shorthorn	1200	15,000	3.33	3.32	4.89	12.90

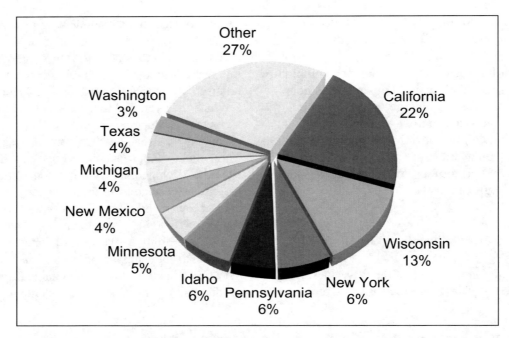

Fig. 7.7   Top ten states in production of cow's milk during 2008. (USDA, National Agricultural Statistics Service)

and manufacturing plants to produce the majority of the country's manufactured milk products, including over a fourth of the total cheese produced.

Since 1970 milk production per cow has increased over 50%, while the number of dairy cows has decreased 24% and the average herd size per operation has increased. Most dairies in the United States fall within two broad categories: traditional or large scale specialized dairies. The traditional dairy consists of less than two hundred cows and equates to the average herd size a family could accommodate and still retain satisfactory living standards while maintaining a functioning farm, including growing feed for the cattle. In 2008, 32.5% of total United States milk production was attributed to traditional dairying systems. For states including Pennsylvania and Wisconsin, these traditional dairies dominate the industry contributing up to 74% and 56% of total milk produced, respectively. The second category of specialized dairy systems represents operations dominated by herd sizes greater than two hundred cows. Operations that exceed five hundred cows are classified as concentrated animal operations and are subject to regulation by the Environmental Protection Agency. Herd sizes of 200–499 contribute to 12.6% of total milk produced, whereas dairies of herd size of five hundred or greater

represent 54.9% of total milk production. These enterprises may still represent family farms or family corporations, but are specialized in the production of milk and often buy the majority or all of the feed necessary to maintain the herd. Specialized operations are usually found in the newly emerging dairy states such as California, New Mexico, Arizona, Texas, Idaho, and Florida. In California and Idaho, operations with greater than five hundred cows contribute to 92% of the states total milk produced. From the beginning, these larger enterprises were able to adopt business techniques, management strategies, and labor-saving technologies that smaller operations could not afford; resulting in lower milk production costs that have given the larger corporations a competitive advantage. For the traditional dairy operation, producers often belong to cooperatives that assemble and distribute the milk to the processors and manufacturers; however, even the cooperatives are experiencing consolidation and seeing a decrease in number with an increase in size. It should be noted, that although the total number of dairy farms continues to decrease, the herd size of both traditional and specialized dairy operations has experienced growth, whereas the average herd size of traditional dairies was twenty-five cows in 1960 it was eighty-eight in 2000. Currently, traditional dairy enter-

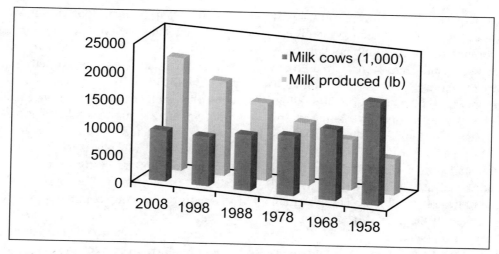

■ **Fig. 7.8**   In the last fifty years the number of milk cows has decreased whereas total milk produced per cow has increased. (USDA, National Agricultural Statistics Service)

prises dominate the industry in terms of number of producers, whereas a majority of milk originates from large scale specialized operations. Both traditional and large dairy conglomerates are predominantly family owned and operated, which is likely to continue to restrict ownership and partnerships to family members.

Management Systems

Types of Dairy Systems

Types of dairy operations include traditional confinement and grazing-based systems. Traditional confinement systems rely on cows being housed year round. Grazing systems are defined as those that meet 30% of the animals forage needs by grazing and provide fresh pasture at least once every three days. Currently, approximately 90% of dairy operations are managed as traditional confinement systems. The size of the herd influences the dairying system, only 1% of herds greater than five hundred practices grazing, whereas approximately 10% of herds less than five hundred practice grazing-based dairying. In traditional confinement systems, females are maintained in various stages of lactation throughout the year, which provides for continual income. The rate of milk production is greater per cow compared to grazing systems; however, the cost of hired labor is greater as well. Because of the need to house animals throughout the year, traditional confinement dairies experience increased capital in-

vestment and are associated with increased feet and leg problems. Nutrition is commonly maintained through the provision of total mixed rations; balanced rations of forages, concentrates, proteins, vitamins, and minerals that meet the nutrient needs of the animal in one feed source. Approximately, 52% of all traditional confinement dairies use total mixed rations, with 36% of dairies of herd sizes less than one hundred employing the feeding strategy and 94% of dairies with herd sizes greater than five hundred feeding total mixed rations. The grazing-based system is defined by the consumption of forages directly harvested by grazing cows and is reliant on forage availability and management practices. Supplemental feed is required to provide optimal nutrient ratios for milk yield and requires an understanding of the grazing behaviors demonstrated by cattle and seasonal changes in pasture quality. Grazing-based dairying may be seasonal, relying on available pasture and synchronization of breeding and lactation cycles, or year round with the feeding of harvested forage during winter months. Although the average pounds of milk produced per cow is less in a grazing-based system, the income generated is comparable to that of traditional confinement systems, in part due to reduced facility and waste handling costs.

Dairy Housing Systems

The two most common types of dairy housing in traditional confinement dairies are tie stall/stanchion barns and free stall barns, which represent 49.2% and 32.6%, respectively, of the housing systems employed. Outdoor and indoor lot group housing facilities, as well as individual pen systems, are used to a lesser extent by the industry. Whereas tie stall facilities are commonly used by small herds of less than one hundred, herds greater than five hundred animals rely on freestall systems in 75% of the operations.

In a tie stall/stanchion system, each cow is confined to an individual stall and is held in its stall through the use of ties or stanchions. The system restricts the movement of the animal from its individual stall. In a tie stall system, a collar, chain, or strap, is placed around the cow's neck and is fastened to the front of the stall. Stanchion structures rely on restraint of the animal by a metal yoke or pivoting bars. Restraint to individual stalls facilitates better health care through continued observation for signs of disease or illness and ease of treatment through confined space. In addition, animals are more easily restrained for breeding and feeding. However, this system is more labor intensive as effort is needed for the addition and release of each cow from its stall. This system also is more difficult to use in conjunction with the traditional milking parlor because of the manual need to release each cow. In smaller herds where a milking parlor is not used, the milking must take place within the stalls. This requires the producer to assume a stooping position during milking and may require manual transport of the milk to storage.

Freestall barns were first constructed in the 1960s to take advantage of aspects of tie stall facilities and group housing lots. In this system individual resting stalls are provided, but the cow is not restrained to an individual stall. Cows have freedom of movement and may enter or leave any stall upon their choosing. It is common to have 10% more cows than stalls as all cows do not rest at the same time. Separate from the stall area is a milking facility and designated community feeding area. Free stall barns are advantageous for use with milking parlors as cows are easily moved into the milking facility. The communal feeding area allows for easier feeding of a group compared to the labor of individualized feeding. Freestall systems require less bedding than conventional stall barns and are associated with reduced feet, leg, and udder damage. Some cows will not use the provided stalls and must be trained to enter them. The individualized attention afforded to cows in a tie stall barn is lost with the freestall housing system and competition at feeding is increased, increasing the risks for injury.

Waste Management Systems

With an increase in herd size of animals maintained in traditional confinement systems, waste management is a growing concern. Improper waste management is associated with the pollution of air, land, streams, lakes, and underground water supplies. Dairy cattle produce approximately 8% of their body weight in manure and 3% in urine each day, allowing a mature cow to produce one hundred twenty pounds of manure and forty-three pounds of urine daily. Manure must be removed from the barn regularly and can be accomplished through the use of alley scrapers (mechanical or tractor), gutter cleaners,

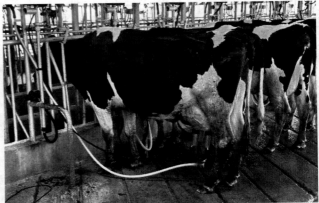

■ **Fig. 7.9** Stanchion dairying system. (Both images © Nitipong Ballapavanich, 2009. Under license from Shutterstock, Inc.)

alley flushing (using fresh or recycled water), slotted floor, or manure vacuum. Facility designs are associated with specific manure handling methods. Approximately 83% of tie stall/stanchion operations rely on a gutter cleaner to remove waste from the housing area, whereas, manure is handled by alley scrappers in 72% of freestall facilities. The majority of dairy operators apply removed waste to rented or owned land. The waste may be applied daily, which is the lowest-cost method of handling, or stored for future hauling. Daily application is weather dependent. Runoff from frozen or snow-covered ground contributes to pollution through the loss of fertilizer nutrients, whereas application during wet weather can be detrimental to ground cover, impacting future crop yields. Manure storage can be accomplished through below-ground storage tanks, earthen basins, or above-ground silos. The size of the storage area is dependent on the number of cows in the herd and the length of time the waste is to be held. Once the storage facility meets its capacity, the manure is applied to land.

Milking Systems

The removal of milk from the lactating female is the primary objective of a dairy operation. Considerable time is invested in the milking process as cows must be milked at regular intervals each day for optimal milk production. Over 90% of dairy operations milk cows twice daily, milking three times daily is practiced to a lesser extent. The removal of milk from the udder occurs under the application of a vacuum to the teat. Pressure in the udder is created by the ejection of milk from the alveoli; the milking machine is maintained at a lower pressure to promote milk flow. Prior to milking, the cows must be prepped, requiring the milking operator to wash, dry and massage the teat for twenty to thirty seconds. This preparation is important toward reducing environmental pathogens on the teat surface and promoting milk let down. Milking begins

■ **Fig. 7.10** Freestall barns. (© Laila Kazakevica, 2009. Under license from Shutterstock, Inc.)

are converted into a nutrient dense food for humans. When cattle are fed grain, the quality and palatability of the beef is increased, efficiency of production is enhanced, and year-round production of beef is achieved. Major seasonal fluctuations in the availability of beef for human consumption do not occur in the United States. Of all domestic livestock, cattle are the most numerous with 1.4 billion head reported worldwide and it is believed that every country in the world has at least some cattle. It is also estimated that there is one cow for every 4.6 people in the world and there are 26.6 head of cattle per square mile of the land surface on Earth.

Beef Cattle Management Systems

The structure of the beef industry varies from some of the other livestock industries as it is typically divided into more distinct segments. Animals are typically owned by multiple individuals or companies as they move from one stage of production to the next. Also, regions of the country often tend to specialize in only one or two segments of the beef industry. The four major segments of the beef industry are purebred producers, commercial cow-calf producers, yearling or stocker operators, and feedlot finishing operations.

Purebred

In purebred production, the primary objective is to produce breeding stock and primarily bulls to be used to mate with commercial cows. This makes purebred production the only segment of the beef industry where the primary goal is not to produce cattle for the purpose of meat consumption. These animals will ultimately be harvested for meat, but only after they have been used to produce breeding stock or used to mate with cows in commercial production. In the purebred production segment, the greatest demand is for bulls. Bulls are generally purebreds whose genetic information derived from pedigree, individual and sibling performance and progeny performance is used to calculate estimates of genetic merit called Expected Progeny Differences (EPDs). These estimates of breeding value are used to aid in the selection process for sires and increase the predictability and efficiency of offspring. Through the marketing of bulls to commercial producers and other purebred producers genetic change in the beef industry is directed by this segment of the industry. Purebred producers that raise exceptionally high-quality cattle

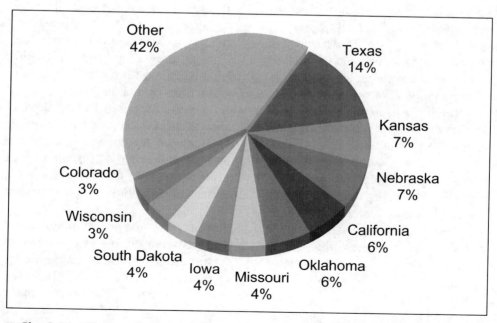

■ **Fig. 8.11**   Top ten states in beef cattle production during 2008. (USDA, National Agricultural Statistics Service)

■ Fig. 8.12 Commercial cow-calf production is the first phase of beef cattle production, which supplies weaned calves to stocker or feedlot operations. (© Bill McKelvie, 2009. Under license from Shutterstock, Inc.)

■ Fig. 8.13 In the United States the majority of beef cattle are finished in feedlot operations. (© Thoma, 2009. Under license from Shutterstock, Inc.)

also market semen and embryos to other cattle producers or sell or lease bulls to stud.

Commercial Cow-Calf

Commercial cow-calf production represents the first phase that produces animals intended for meat consumption. Commercial cow-calf producers typically produce calves that are six to ten months of age and three hundred to seven hundred pounds which are weaned and sold to either a feedlot or a stocker-calf operation. These calves would typically be crossbred and intended for harvest as beef. The goal of most commercial cow-calf producers is to produce the heaviest calves possible with the least cost. The calving season for these operations is usually in the spring or fall. The calving season is generally chosen based upon the availability of feed, environment, management expertise and options, and marketing avenues for the calves. A majority of calves are born in the spring in order to match the rapid forage production in pastures during this season with the peak lactational demands of the dam. While most producers sell their calves at weaning, some will retain ownership of their calves and add additional weight to the animals. Calves sold at weaning typically go to either a feedlot or to a stocker production system. Most producers will retain the top 20–50% of heifer calves to use to replace mature females in the herd that have reached the end of their productive lifetime.

Stocker

Yearling or stocker operations are one of the two destinations of calves at weaning. In this phase, calves are grown to heavier weights on low-priced feedstuffs for six to eighteen months before the calves are placed in feedlots to be fattened for harvest. Stocker operations generally purchase their calves from commercial cow-calf producers and grow them on forages or crop residues and eventually sell them to feedlots. The feed utilized in stocker operations varies by region and producer and may include summer pastures and range, small-grain pastures, crop residues, by-products of production of food for humans, by-products of ethanol production, or standing prairie hay or silage. For cattle with less growth potential, this period allows them to grow in stature and muscling before they move into the feedlot and prevents over-fattening of these animals in the feedlot. In cattle with high growth potential, it is more efficient to place these animals directly into feedlots at weaning.

Feedlots (Finishing or Fattening)

Feedlots represent the last phase of the production system for live animals. Cattle are typically fed to an endpoint based upon their body fat composition, thus this segment of the industry may be referred to as the fattening or finishing phase. Cattle are fed to the desired endpoint on grain-based diets and then sent to be harvested by packers. Both heifers and steers, and recently weaned calves or yearlings from stocker operations are fed in feedlots. These cattle typically enter this phase between six hundred and one thousand pounds of body weight and are harvested between one thousand and fifteen hundred pounds of body weight. Cattle are fed in a feedlot for between sixty to two hundred days and a vast majority of young cattle in the United States are finished on grain in feedlots before being sent to harvest. Feedlots vary greatly in size from very small operations that either purchase calves or raise them from birth, to very large operations that concentrate tens of thousands of cattle in operations specializing only in feeding cattle for harvest. Feedlots sell finished cattle to packer/processor operations for harvest and processing. The packer/processor sells carcasses or boxed beef to retailers, distributors, HRI (Hotels, Restaurants, and Institutions), or for export. Retailers and distributors then further process these larger primal cuts for sale to the consumer. Over the last few decades, feedlots and meat packing plants have increased in size, while simultaneously decreasing in number. While the beef industry can be divided into these various segments, they are not always a clear-cut delineation. It is not unusual for a producer to own their cattle through more than one phase, by either keeping them on their farm or contracting with other farms to fatten or finish their cattle

■ **Fig. 8.14**   Pneumonia is a multifactorial disease that mostly affects calves, but can affect cattle of all ages. (© ason, 2009. Under license from Shutterstock, Inc.)

Health Management

The movement of beef cattle from one stage of production to the next contributes to bovine respiratory disease, which is the most economically devastating health concern in the industry. Young animals are susceptible to pneumonia, and economic losses arise from treatment cost, failure to thrive, reduced weight gain, and ultimately death. The disease is multifactorial and both microorganisms and management practices are known to contribute to the onset. Pneumonia is representative of inflammation of the lungs and results in reduced respiratory capacity. Death is the result of inability to breathe due to lung damage. Both viruses and bacteria can trigger pneumonia. The severity of respiratory infection and resulting lung damage differs between the microorganisms, with viral origins of the disease being more detrimental. The microorganisms involved also make the calf more

susceptible to secondary infections. A reduction in feed intake is one of the earliest observations of the disease; this is followed by coughing, thick nasal discharge, and overall unthrifty appearance. Antibiotic treatment is often successful and management control practices to minimize stress of the calf are important toward reducing the incidence of pneumonia within the herd.

Capacity of Production

The goal of the beef industry is to satisfy consumer demand for palatable, tender, consistent, edible meat. Animals may be raised for market or retained for breeding. Females in the breeding herd will be bred between thirteen and fifteen months of age. After an approximately 285 day gestation, the heifer will calve for the first time at approximately twenty-four months of age. Females are bred to produce their next calf approximately eighty days after giving birth, resulting in the production of one calf each year. This annual cycle will continue until the female is removed from the breeding herd. Cows are removed or culled from the breeding herd for a variety of reasons including failure to become pregnant in a timely manner, feet or leg problems, udder problems that impair the ability of the calf to suckle, age,

■ **Fig. 8.15** Beef carcasses are graded according to quality and yield. Fat is a primary factor in determining both grades. Whereas quality is assessed by the degree of intramuscular fat, backfat and internal fat are used to assess yield. (© svitlana10, 2009. Under license from Shutterstock, Inc.)

temperament and productivity. On average, beef cows remain in the herd for six to seven years of age. Once a cow is culled, she is sent to be harvested. Weaning in the beef industry occurs between five and nine months of age and cattle will reach market weight at eighteen to twenty-four months of age.

Beef Cattle as a Food Commodity

The primary end products of beef production are derived from grain-fed cattle that are between twelve and thirty months of age. The carcasses of animals that represent this primary product are graded for both quality of the beef and the yield of beef from the carcass. Quality grades used for the primary product are prime, choice, select, standard, and utility, with prime being the most desirable quality grade. Quality grades are based primarily on the amount of intramuscular fat or marbling that is present within the loin muscle of the carcass. Age of the animal and color of the meat are also factors used to calculate quality grade. Yield grades provide an estimate of the percentage of the carcass that will be lean meat relative to content of fat. Yield grades are based upon the amount of backfat on the carcass, the cross-sectional area of the loin or longissumus dorsi muscle at the twelfth rib, carcass weight and the amount of internal (kidney, pelvic and heart) fat. Yield grades are from one to five. A carcass with a yield grade of one is from an animal with minimal backfat and that is heavy muscled that will have a high yield of edible beef. A carcass on the other end of the range with a yield grade of five would have excessive backfat, would be light muscled and would have a much lower yield of edible beef. The most valuable beef carcass would have a quality grade of prime and a yield grade of one. Meat from animals that are culled from the production herd, such as cows and bulls that are older than thirty months, are a secondary product of beef production, and represents about 20% of the beef produced in the United States. These secondary products are used in ground beef, processed beef products and in lower quality steaks and roasts.

Nutritional Value of Beef

The United States beef cattle population peaked in 1976, this marked a gradual decline in annual per capita beef consumption that would persist for

■ **Fig. 8.16**   Beef remains an integral part of many diets. (© Gregory Gerber, 2009. Under license from Shutterstock, Inc.)

nearly twenty years. In the last ten years, per capita consumption has remained steady. Explanation for earlier decline can be attributed to the concern over cholesterol intake in the late 1970s and early 1980s. During this time, researches tended to over emphasize the negative health effects of cholesterol, explaining the decrease in red meat consumption. However, current research has shown that cholesterol in moderation is not detrimental and the stigma attached to red meat has slowly declined, thus explaining the recent, higher per capita consumption. Beef is a nutritious food, and lean beef can be included as a part of a balanced diet. Concerns by consumers regarding the fat content of beef, especially in comparison to other meat and protein sources, have been addressed by trimming of excess fat before retail sale and by genetic selection for leaner cattle. Variation in beef quality due to the various approaches taken to achieve the end product remains a concern by consumers.

Small Ruminants

This chapter introduces the classification of sheep and goat breeds in the United States, including fiber, meat, and dairy types and the prominent breeds that fall under each category are described. Production systems and managerial aspects of the goat and sheep enterprises are explained, along with the reproductive aspects of both species. Lastly, uses of sheep and goats for fiber, conservation, and food along with the nutritional benefits of sheep and goat meat are described.

SHEEP

"The shepherd always tries to persuade the sheep that their interests and his own are the same."
—Stendhal (1783–1842)

Sheep: A Historical Perspective

Domestication of sheep traces to South West Asia, an area now occupied by modern day Iran and Iraq, and occurred around 8000 B.C. according to archaeological evidence. Sheep are one of the earliest food animals to have begun the process of domestication, which closely coincided with the settlement of humans into communities. Their domestication provided a stable supply of fresh meat as humans shifted from a hunter-gatherer to agrarian society. The wild sheep was an attractable target for domestication due to its relative docility, size, and socially dependent nature, attributes now known to contribute to early domestication success. Modern domestic sheep are descendents of Mouflon sheep, which still exists as a primitive breed of Iran and Iraq today. Although domestication of sheep was originally for a source of food, evidence that specialization of sheep for prod-

ucts such as wool was evident by 3000 B.C. As a means of cultivating the wool rendered from sheep, weaving was one of the first arts to develop and woolen factories began to appear in Rome during 50 A.D. This period of time also corresponds to the development of the Merino breed specifically for the production of fine wool. The sheep also provided milk and capital. Shepherds and their flocks are routinely mentioned throughout the Bible as sheep were of crucial economic importance. As with other livestock, the domesticated sheep was spread throughout the world by migrating human populations.

All ancestors of domesticated sheep found in the United States were introduced. Rocky Mountain sheep, also known as Big Horn sheep, are native to the continent and served no role in the development of the United States sheep industry. Christopher Columbus was the first to introduce sheep into the Western Hemisphere during his second voyage to the New World in 1493. Sheep were brought to the West again by Cortez in 1519. These sheep were used by early Spanish settlers and armies as they moved to conquer and colonize the New World. Subsequently, flocks were acquired by Native Americans and these sheep became the Navajo-Churro sheep breed of today. The introduction of sheep by English colonizers occurred in 1607 and again in 1609 by the Jamestown colony in modern day Virginia. Initial imports were primarily for food and wool quality declined during this era. However, the wool industry would begin to develop coincident with the first woolen mill in Massachusetts during 1662. As wool gained importance in America during the seventeenth century, labor laws were enacted requiring colonists to work in the industry. England, enraged by the growing status of the colonist's wool industry outlawed the American wool trade, which contributed to events that prompted the Revolutionary War.

■ **Fig. 9.1.1** Domesticated sheep are descendants of the Mouflon. (© Fernec jCegledi, 2009. Under license from Shutterstock, Inc.)

■ **Fig. 9.1.2** In Massachusetts, early law required that every young person learn the art of spinning and weaving wool. (© akva, 2009. Under license from Shutterstock, Inc.)

By the mid 1800s, the sheep industry started drifting westward as expansive, untapped, and cheap land became available. The Civil War contributed to the greatest wool demand in American history. Shortly after, however, the United States wool industry began to face competition from imported wool and cotton. The emphasis of the industry began to shift away from wool production and into raising and marketing lambs for food. The greatest number of sheep coincided with World War II, after this time sheep numbers began to dramatically decline, a trend that continues today. Peak sheep numbers during War World II are attributed to the supply of mutton as a dietary staple to soldiers during the war. Post World War II, lower returns per investment, scarcity of sheep herders, uncertainties of grazing allotments on public land, susceptibility to predation, and seasonal production and fluctuations in annual income have contributed to the decline of the industry. The National Wool Act of 1950, which demanded increased production of wool as a strategic material for military uniforms, stabilized the industry until the 1960s, when wool was removed as a strategic material and cheap, synthetically engineered material began to replace the need of wool as a fabric. Although the industry has attempted to capitalize on meat production, challenges have been faced in part to lack of incorporation of lamb in the consumer's diet. For those who do consume lamb, it is a high priced commodity when compared with other meats available. The decline in sheep numbers has occurred to the extent that sheep were labeled as a minor agricultural species by the Federal Drug Administration in 1990. Further insult came in 1995 as the federal government withdrew its subsidies to wool producers. The future of the sheep industry will ultimately be determined by consumer demand, which is driven by availability of convenient and user friendly cuts, increased knowledge of preparation and cooking, and improved consistency in retail products. Furthermore, tapping into alternative markets including value added products and the fast-food industry are needed for market expansion.

Breeds of Sheep

Approximately two hundred breeds of sheep are documented in the world today. According to the

■ **Fig. 9.1.3**   During Woodrow Wilson's term (1912), sheep were kept on the White House lawn. The wool was auctioned off to support charities and the small flock also helped to trim the lawn. (Library of Congress)

American Sheep Industry Association, only forty-seven breeds of sheep are found in the United States. Breeds of sheep are classified according to their commercial use and include: maternal and paternal breeds, dual-purpose breeds, hair breeds, and dairy breeds. Breeds vary considerably in weight and number of offspring. Weight may range from one hundred to four hundred pounds, whereas, number of offspring may range from one to six per lambing depending on the breed type. Universally, sheep are considered the most timid and least trainable of the domesticated species. These features have prompted the assumption that sheep are the least intelligent of the animals; however, these attributes are due to early selection based on herding or flocking instincts. The sociable and group mindset of the flock is desired by the shepherd, but discourages independent behavior. This has left the sheep more reliant on human care relative to other domesticated animals.

Maternal Breeds

Maternal, or ewe, breeds are classified according to reproductive efficiency rates, maternal ability, wool production, and milk production. These breeds are typically white faced and include the Merino, Rambouillet, and Finnsheep.

The Merino breed was developed during the reign of the Roman Empire between 41 and 50 A.D. in an area occupied now by Spain. Considered the most influential breed of sheep, the Merino traces its origins to Tarentine and Laodician sheep, breeds of Rome and Asia Minor, respectively. They have played a crucial role as the foundation breed for the development of almost all other fine wool sheep breeds in existence today. During the fall of the Roman Empire, England and Spain rose to become world leaders in Merino production. Spain, considered to provide the finest Merino wool in the world, outlawed the exportation of Merino sheep to maintain its status as the producer of the greatest quality wool in the world and its hold on the industry. This law remained in effect until 1809, when Spain was invaded by Napolean Bonaparte. William Foster would risk penalty of Spanish laws in 1793 to smuggle the Merino breed to America. The Merino is medium bodied, produces a high quality white fleece, is able to thrive on relatively poor grazing land, and is known for its strong flocking instincts.

There are multiple types of Merino sheep developed throughout the world. In the United States Merinos are characterized by their excess skin that increases surface area for wool production and are classified as A, B, or C types according to size and quantity of wool produced as a result of skin folding. The A and B types are heavy types, with the A type possessing heavy neck folds and wrinkling of the hide. The B type also carries heavy neck folds, but is relatively free of wrinkles in the hide. The heavy folding of the skin as occurs with these types creates difficulty in shearing, may result in a lower quality fleece, and promotes parasite infestations. Limited production of A and B types occurs within the United States and the focus has been toward the C type, or Delaine Merino, which is a smooth or nearly smooth type. The Delaine Merino is of medium size with ewes weighing one hundred twenty-five to one hundred eight pounds and rams one hundred seventy-five to two hundred thirty-five pounds.

The Rambouillet breed originated in France in the late 1700s and was developed using Spanish Merino lines. However, the Rambouillet was selected for greater size over its Merino ancestors and breeding records trace to 1801 in France. The importation of the Rambouillet into the United States occurred around 1840 and it is estimated that 50% of the United States crossbred sheep population today were influenced by Rambouillet breeding. Today, the Rambouillet is the seventh most popular breed of sheep in the United States, prevalent in the western states and preferred as a producer of fine wool. This breed is large bodied with the mature weight of ewes ranging from one hundred fifty to two hundred pounds and the weight of rams two hundred fifty to three hundred pounds. Rambouillets are fast growing, produce a high quality white fleece, and are adequately muscled, contributing to the dual classification as a maternal breed and dual-purpose breed of sheep.

■ **Fig. 9.1.5** Rambouillet. (Courtesy The American Rambouillet Sheep Breeders Association)

■ **Fig. 9.1.4** Merino. (© John Carnemolla, 2009. Under license from Shutterstock, Inc.)

■ **Fig. 9.1.6** Finnsheep. (Courtesy Elizabeth H. Kinne, Stillmeadow Finnsheep, DeRuyter, NY)

The Finnsheep, also known as the Finnish Landrace, originated in Finland. First importations into the United States occurred in 1966 and although further importations since this time have been limited, the breed has gained popularity in the United States in recent years. The breed is renowned for multiple births, commonly producing three or more offspring per lambing. However, Finnsheep display a reduced growth rate relative to other maternal breeds, reach maturity at an early age, and are of small mature size. Females average one hundred twenty to one hundred ninety pounds at maturity, whereas males average one hundred fifty to two hundred pounds. The breed is polled and wool is of medium quality and not as desired as that originating from the Merino or Rambouillet breeds, however, the fleece is high yielding. The breed is commonly utilized in crossbreeding programs to improve reproductive characteristics and overall lambing rates.

Paternal Breeds

Paternal, or ram, breeds are defined according to growth rates and carcass characteristics. Ram breeds are usually dark faced and further classified by the weight of the offspring at market, which includes heavy, medium, and light weight types. The Suffolk and Hampshire are popular ram breeds of the United States that produce heavy weight lambs for market.

The Suffolk breed originated in southern England from the breeding of Southdown and Norfolk Horned sheep. First importations in the United States occurred in 1888. It is currently the most popular breed of sheep in United States registries. The breed is white woolen and characterized by black face, ears, and legs that are free from wool. A large bodied breed with mature ewes weighing one hundred eighty to two hundred fifty pounds and mature rams two hundred fifty to three hundred fifty pounds, Suffolk are polled, display prominent muscling, and produce rapidly growing, lean muscled offspring. Selected for carcass quality, Suffolk yields a light-weight quality fleece that contains black fibers, elements that detract from its market value.

The Hampshire originated in England and was imported into the United States in the mid 1800s, prior to the Civil War. These original imports were lost during the war and subsequent imports of 1880 served as the foundation for the breed in the United States. Today, the breed is the second most populous breed of sheep in the United States. Hampshires resemble the Suffolk in both size and marking similarities; however, the Hampshire tends to be smaller and has a dark brown face, ears, and legs. At maturity, ewes weigh a minimum of two hundred pounds, whereas the minimum mature weight of rams is two hundred seventy-five pounds. Wool of Hampshires extends onto the legs and head giving rise to a wool cap. As the wool is of similar quality

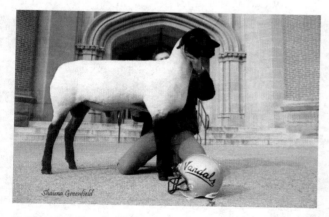

■ **Fig. 9.1.7** Suffolk. (Courtesy Paul Kuber, The Ohio State University)

■ **Fig. 9.1.8** Hampshire. (Courtesy Paul Kuber, The Ohio State University)

■ **Fig. 9.1.9**   Dorset. (© Paul Cowan, 2009. Under license from Shutterstock, Inc.)

■ **Fig. 9.1.10**   Columbia. (© Steve Shoup, 2009. Under license from Shutterstock, Inc.)

as the Suffolk and of little market value, the increased wool of Hampshires is not desired. Hampshires are efficient utilizers of forage and the rapid growth weight of lambs, usually gaining a pound or more per day till marketing, contributes to this breeds use in the meat industry.

Dual-Purpose Breeds

Breeds that produce both wool and meat of acceptable quality are termed dual-purpose breeds. The wool and carcass produced by these breeds are of lesser quality relative to the maternal and paternal breeds, respectively, but both products are adequately produced in one animal. The dual-purpose breeds include the Dorset, Polypay, and Columbia.

The Dorset originated in the counties of Dorset and Somerset, England. The breed was first imported into the western United States in 1860 and the eastern United States in 1885. The Dorset is now the third most popular breed of sheep in American registration numbers. The breed has a white face, ears, and legs that lack a woolen covering. The breed may be horned or polled with the number of polled Dorsets currently exceeding the number of horned. The polled trait results from a mutation of the horned breed first identified and selected for in a flock from North Carolina in the 1900s. The ewes are known for their prolificacy, milk production, and their ability to breed out of season and reach mature weights of one hundred fifty to two hundred pounds. Rams weigh two hundred twenty-five to two hundred seventy-five at maturity. The ability to breed out of season is the single most important quality that contributes to the breed's popularity. Most of

the demand for out of season lambs lies in the eastern United States; hence, most Dorsets are raised on the east side of the Mississippi River. The wool is of a medium grade and its carcass traits are average.

The Polypay breed was developed in 1968 at the United States Sheep Experiment Station at Dubois, Idaho and is a composite breed of Finnsheep, Rambouillet, Targhee, and Dorset breeding. The breed was developed to meet the goal of lifetime prolificacy, ability for ewes to lamb at least twice per year, production of rapidly growing lambs, and a high quality carcass. It was the intent of the breeders to develop more productive sheep that promote the declining industry. The name Polypay was meant to insinuate that this breed of sheep could produce more than two paying goods per year, fleece and two lamb crops. The Polypay is characterized by early maturity and is a medium sized sheep with a white face, ears, and legs. The wool covering extends onto the top of the head and down the legs of the sheep.

The Columbia breed was developed by the Bureau of Animal Industry at the King Ranch in Laramie, Wyoming in 1912. Developed from the crossing of Rambouillet ewes with Lincoln rams, it is now the eighth most popular breed of sheep in the United States. The goal during breed development was to replace cross-breeding practices on the range by providing a true breeding type that maximized wool and lamb production. With ewes weighing one hundred fifty to two hundred twenty-five pounds and rams two hundred twenty-five to three hundred pounds, these animals are well suited for life on the range in the northwestern regions and are adequately suited to pastures of the Midwest. The ewes

■ **Fig. 9.1.11**   Katahdin. (© Sajko, 2009. Under license from Shutterstock, Inc.)

are adequately fertile, good mothers, and produce acceptable market lambs. Columbians are polled and white with woolen face and legs.

Hair Breeds

All sheep have a combination of woolen fibers and hair fibers. Primitive breeds of sheep are distinguished by their hair fibers that mask the undercoat of woolen fibers, which provide warmth. The majority of sheep breeds were selected and bred to maximize the presence of woolen fibers and minimize the hair fiber. However, in arid climates there is relatively little need for wool and the sheep in these parts of the world have been selected for an emphasis on hair fiber that naturally shed in response to the climate, which negates the need of shearing. Although these animals may resemble goats, they are indeed of sheep decent and are raised for their meat. The tropical sheep have exceptional fertility rates, viability, parasite resistance, and extended breeding seasons. However, these sheep have reduced growth rates, lighter mature weights, and re-

duced carcass merit. The two most globally utilized hair sheep breeds include the Barbados Blackbelly and Saint Croix, whereas the Katahdin is the most common hair sheep of the United States and is sixth in registrations. The Katahdin traces its origins to Maine. Named after Mount Katahdin, the highest peak in Maine, the breed was developed for land management to graze power line easements as an alternative to spraying or mowing. Multiple breeds of sheep including the St. Croix, Tunis, Southdown, Hampshire, Suffolk, and Wiltshire Horn have influenced the Katahdin, which is known for its adaptability, exceptional maternal qualities, adequate carcass, and low maintenance as they do not require shearing.

Dairy Breeds

Just as sheep breeds were developed to meet the demands for meat and fiber, specialized breeds have been developed for the dairy industry as well. Dairy sheep breeds include East Friesian, Awassi, Assaf, Lancaune, Sarda, Manchega, and Chios. These breeds are exceptional milk producers that produce four hundred to eleven hundred pounds of milk per lactation, but are not readily available in the United States. East Friesian is noted as the highest producing dairy breed and is the only dairy breed introduced into the United States, although importations have been limited. The United States dairy industry is reliant on adapting currently available sheep breeds for milk production and includes the use of Dorset, Polypay, and Rideau Arcott breeds. These breeds are inferior to the specialized dairy breeds of European and Mideastern countries, producing only one hundred to two hundred pounds of milk per lactation. The Rideau Arcott was developed in Canada and is predominantly influenced by Finnsheep, Suffolk, and East Friesian breeding. Originally created for improved lambing rates, the breed is noted to routinely give birth to triplets and lambs every eight months.

United States Sheep Industry

Currently, the sheep industry accounts for less than 1% of cash receipts received from livestock enterprises. Peak sheep numbers occurred in the mid 1880s and were reported at 51 million head. Since this time, the number of sheep raised in the United

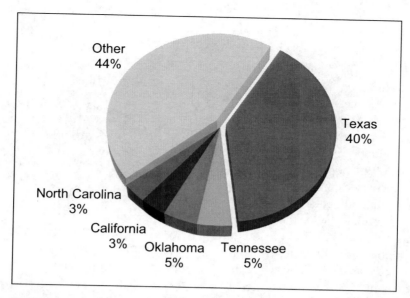

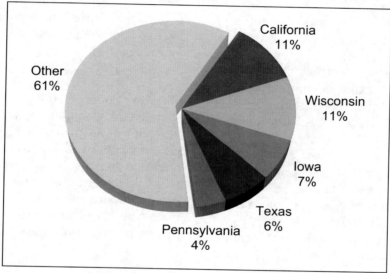

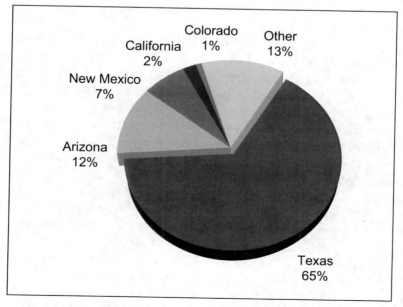

■ **Fig. 9.2.6** Top five states in goats used (clockwise) for meat, milk, and mohair during 2008. (USDA, National Agricultural Statistics Service)

Texas. Between 1997 and 2002, Angora goat numbers fell substantially. However, total goat numbers increased 24% as a consequence of increases in the number of meat and milk goats, which increased 87% and 54%, respectively. The overall upward trend of the United States goat industry in part is due to the changing demographics of the population. Ethnic diversity, gender, and increased interests in hobby farming have had substantial influences on the industry. Ethnic diversity is a primary factor that has contributed to the growing goat industry. The most influential ethnic populations are Hispanic, Muslim, Caribbean, and Chinese. The goat industry of the southern and western United States is expected to continue expansion in response to the increasing immigrant populations of these regions. The number of women owned goat farms increased 34% between 1997 and 2002 with the greatest increases occurring in Delaware, Tennessee, and Kentucky. Ownership of small ruminants in both small scale dairying and fiber production has been a female dominated production practice in recent years as women seek opportunities to participate in agricultural industries. Additional potential for sustained growth arises from observations in the average ages of goat operators. Goat farming is conducive to smaller farming practices and inviting to individuals returning to rural communities and visiting farming as a hobby. Over 43% of goat operators are over the age of fifty-five and less than 30% are under the age of forty-four.

Goat Management Systems

Goat enterprises consist primarily of purebred and commercial operations. The goal of the purebred operation is to specialize in providing a specific breed, while maintaining the breeds quality and integrity. In the meat goat industry, limited purebred operations exist in the United States, impart due to the meat goat breeds being developed in Africa and New Zealand and few imports made into the United States. In the dairy industry, increased importance placed on registered and pedigreed animals has increased involvement in purebred operations. The need for registered dairy goats originates from the emphasis placed on the show animal that is ideal in conformation and milk production. Commercial operations are increasing in number in the meat industry, though limited in the dairy industry. Less than

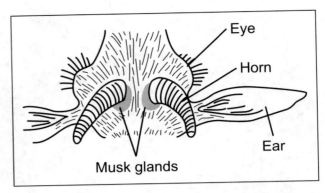

■ Fig. 9.2.7 Male goats naturally mark their territory through musk glands, which are located on the crown of their head, overlapping the horn bud. Removal of the musk glands, known as deodorizing, is performed during the debudding process by making two additional burns with the debudding iron in the area of the musk glands.

thirty-five commercial goat dairies are reported. In commercial operations, either non-registered purebred animals are maintained or crossbreeding strategies are utilized to improve the characteristics of marketed animals. Most meat goat operations have relied on the infusion of Boer goat genetics to improve carcass quality. The dairy industry will utilize meat-type bucks to improve the marketability of dairy offspring for the meat markets.

Capacity of Production

Most dairy goat breeds are seasonally polyestrus, displaying estrous cycle regularity averaging twenty-one days when the period of light decreases within the photoperiod. Exceptions include the dwarf goats, which are non-seasonal. Non-seasonal estrous cycles are common amongst fiber and meat breeds as well. Kidding occurs following a one hundred fifty day gestation period. Multiple births are dependent on the breed. Boer goats are known to routinely twin, whereas triplets and quadruplets are common to the Nigerian dwarf breed. Length of lactation is breed dependent as well. Boer goats average lactations of four months in length, whereas the lactation of the dairy breeds is commonly ten months. For the dairy goat, peak milk production is coincident with the third or fourth lactation and the doe can produce up to eight pounds of milk per day

■ **Fig. 9.2.8**   In the early twentieth century goat milk was consumed predominantly by the lower class as goats were viewed as the poor man's cow. In recent years, there has been a resurgence in the use of goat's milk to manufacture cheese sought by the artisanal food movement. (Library of Congress)

during this time. Male horned goats posses musk glands, located on the crown of the head overlapping the horn bud. These glands are responsible for the characteristic odor of male goats during the breeding season. Producers may deodorize their bucks by removal of the musk glands; however, when left intact the odor emitted from the glands stimulate estrus in the doe and improves conception. If the doe is being bred to produce milk, the bucks should be kept separate from these does as the odor can taint the milk.

Goat as a Food Commodity

To address the increased domestic demand for goat meat, federally inspected goat harvest increased seven fold between 1983 and 2004 to peak at 670 thousand head. However, live goats marketed for food and freshly harvested goats fall outside the statistics for federally inspected harvests, and therefore, the number of harvested animals is much greater than current estimates. New Jersey and Texas dominate in terms of federally inspected harvests, representing 30% and 18%, respectively, of the total industry. The demand for goat meat is not for individual cuts of meat, but for whole carcass or portions of the carcass including quarters. These larger cuts lend themselves to the traditional cooking methods of slow roasting and stewing. Kids, goats less than one year of age, are harvested between three to five months of age weighing twenty-five to fifty pounds and the meat is marketed as chevon. Meat from kids marketed within the first week of life is termed cabrito and is highly sought by select ethnic populations. Older, or mature, goat meat that sources from goats of the meat, dairy, and fiber industries is used primarily in processed foods. Currently there is no quality grading system in effect for marketed goat meat.

As limited commercial dairy goat enterprises are in operation, the majority of fluid goat milk marketed in the United States originates from California. Increased fat content makes goat milk ideal in the cheese industry and in fact, goat cheese is the most rapidly expanding market of the dairy goat industry. In 2005, there were a reported one hundred goat cheese producers in the United States, most products being marketed through farmers markets, local retailers, and direct sales. Goat's milk can be used to make any type of cheese traditionally made from cow's milk. Popular cheeses made from goat's milk include chevre, feta, and gjetost.

Nutritional Value of Goat Products

As a result of the age of harvest, there is minimal fat covering of the goat carcass, contributing to goat meat as one of the leanest of all domesticated meats. When compared to beef, lamb, and pork it has the lowest amount of total fat, saturated fat, calories, and cholesterol per serving. Goats' milk offers numerous advantages to the consumer when compared to cows' milk. These include: increased concentrations of vitamin A and niacin, greater concentrations of short- and medium-chain fatty acids that are more easily digested by the young and elderly, and reduced allergenic response, and thus it is more tolerated by people with allergies.

Goats for Fiber, Conservation, and Biotechnology

Fiber

Mohair is the cleaned, long, outer hair coat of the Angora goat. Mohair may be divided into three types: kid, young, and adult. The mohair from younger animals is finer and more valuable. After the fourth shearing, Angora goats are traditionally sold for meat as the quality of fiber is decreased. Mohair is smoother than wool, but lacks the felting properties. It is commonly used in upholstery fabrics due to its strength, durability, ability to accept dyes, and flame resistance. Cashmere fiber is obtained predominantly from the Cashmere breed of goat once annually. This soft undercoat begins to grow in late July and is complete in December. The cashmere must be collected before the end of its growth or it will be shed naturally. The cashmere is

■ **Fig. 9.2.9**   Goats are browsers and will consume twigs and young shoots of trees and shrubs. (© ason, 2009. Under license from Shutterstock, Inc.)

■ **Fig. 9.2.10**   Considered stronger than steel, spider web silk is sought after by industries that require a durable, yet lightweight, fiber. Prior to the development of transgenic goats that secrete the spider silk protein in their milk, spider silk fiber was unavailable commercially due to the inability to farm spiders for the product. (© Arthur Eugene Preston, 2009. Under license from Shutterstock, Inc.)

separated from the regular goat hair fiber by combing or using a commercial dehairer. Sixty percent of the world's supply of cashmere is produced in China and the remainder in Turkey, Afghanistan, Iraq, Iran, Kashmere, Australia and New Zealand. It is a new industry for the United States appearing in the last thirty years. Cashmere is fine in texture, soft, light, and resilient. It is considered one the worlds most luxurious fibers; historically documented as the fiber of kings, cashmere was reported to line the Arc of the Covenant in biblical accounts.

Conservation

Similar to the sheep industry, goats may be used for ground cover management to clear brush for fire control, remove invasive weeds and noxious plants, and clear roadways or passageways. Goats are browsers and prefer broadleaf plants, twigs, and young shoots of trees and shrubs, plants not utilized by cattle. The selection of browse by goats and the grazing habits of cattle for mature grasses allow the two species to be companion grazed alongside in the same pasture. Although estimates suggest relatively few operations practice companion grazing, this practice may be used to improve pasture quality and promote plant diversity for sustainable rangeland management, while providing the benefit of dual-income. In the southern United States goats are being used for the management of the invasive Asian vine Kudzu and when compared to sheep, goats are able to more effectively manage and clear brush in significantly less time than sheep.

Goats are being used as pack animals as well, capable of navigating terrain that is less accessible to larger animals including horses, donkeys, and llamas. Goats are easily trained as pack animals when less than one year of age and can sustain 25% of their body weight in pack over five to fifteen miles of mountainous terrain per day. While allowed in National Forests and lands supervised by the Bureau of Land Management, goats are not allowed in National Parks.

Biotechnology

The use of transgenic goats in biotechnology has received considerable attention in the literature. The most wide-spread use is the production of pharmaceuticals that can be harvested from the milk of transgenic lactating females. Products from these animals, however, cannot be used for human consumption. One application of transgenic goats is the production of spider silk. Spider silk, one of the strongest materials in the world, can be used for the manufacture of products ranging from bullet proof clothing to the manufacture of artificial tendons, ligaments, or limbs.

Swine

"I like pigs. Dogs look up to us. Cats look down on us. Pigs treat us as equals."
—*Winston Churchill (1874–1965)*

This chapter introduces the primary swine breeds of the United States, which are categorized as maternal and paternal breeds. The structure of the swine industry and the physical facilities involved in swine production are emphasized, in conjunction with proper health management techniques that ensure maintenance of healthy and productive animals. Lastly, the nutritional benefits of pork and its contribution to the human diet are described.

Swine: A Historical Perspective

According to fossil records, wild pigs are estimated to date forty-five million years ago. However, the domestication of pigs did not occur until 9000 B.C. in Eastern Turkey, 4900 B.C. in China, and as late as 1500 B.C. in Europe. Although archaeologists originally suggested that pigs domesticated at these sites were transported through human migration, it is now suggested that wild pigs were actually domesticated independently by various human settlements. It should be noted that despite evidence that supports the independent domestication of pigs, findings of the migration of pigs with human settlements also exists. Interestingly, most recent evidence suggests that while Eastern Turkey pigs migrated with humans, the domestication of the wild pigs of Europe offered an improved domestic animal that eventually replaced domestic pigs of different ancestral origin, and consequently the domestic pigs of today are considered descendants of the European wild boar.

The pig was first brought West in 1493 by Columbus and supplied a food source during his second voyage to the New World. However, it is Hernando DeSoto that is accredited as being the father of the American pork industry. In 1539, DeSoto brought thirteen hogs to what is now Tampa Bay, Florida. During his three years of exploration, the initial population increased to over seven hundred. Pigs readily revert to a feral state, acquiring the characteristics of the wild ancestors, and it is DeSoto's original swine herd that served as the founder population of the feral razorbacks located in the southern United States.

Pigs were brought to the Jamestown Colony in 1607 by Sir Walter Raleigh. As colonies dispersed throughout the east coast, they took pigs with them. Without confinement semi-feral pigs became a nuisance over time and in Manhattan a wall was constructed to control the roaming animals. Some suggest this wall served as the origin of Wall Street. Records were maintained as early as 1633 documenting the number and weight of marketed swine. These animals were caught by hounds and marketed and shipped as salted pork. There were no efforts to manage product consistency, and the majority of these free roaming animals foraged from fields and forests, with some producers fattening their stock on surplus grain, milk, and excess table waste. These practices began the development of swine as an important agricultural animal. In early history, the pig's primary contribution was lard, rather than meat. The lard was a highly valued commodity and a trend toward the development of breeds of pigs for their ability to generate excessive body fat began. Corn also helped facilitate fat formation in the hogs and a large segment of the corn grown in Tennessee, Ohio, and Kentucky was used in the swine industry and these states became leading swine production centers. Cincinnati, Ohio, flourished from the industry due to its centralized location and distribution of pork by boat along

■ **Fig. 10.1** Domesticated pigs are descendants of the wild boar. (© Eric Isselée, 2009. Under license from Shutterstock, Inc.)

■ **Fig. 10.2** Pig breeds of the United States were originally classified as lard or bacon type. As the market for lard declined post War World II, breeders began to focus on the production of pigs that deemphasized lard and increased lean muscle mass to produce meat type pigs. Lard-type pigs are compact and fatten rapidly on grain. The Guinea hog of North America (pictured) was a popular lard-type hog in the late 1880s early 1900s due to its ease of fattening. Today, its status is listed as critical along with the other two remaining lard-types, the Mulefoot, and the Choctaw. The popularity of these breeds today resides primarily with their use as a companion species. (© Eric Isselée, 2009. Under license from Shutterstock, Inc.)

the Ohio and Mississippi rivers. It was here that the first pork-packing center was constructed in 1850 and the city became known as Porkopolis. By the 1860s, expansion of farming West and the development of the railroad relocated the center of activity to Chicago, Illinois. Chicago remained the primary marketing center until post World War II when marketing decentralized and packing plants were built near areas of production. World War II also marked the development of swine that maximized lean cuts (ham, loin, picnic, and Boston butt) and minimized lard, which was now considered waste.

Breeds of Swine

There are over four hundred breeds of swine reported worldwide; however, only eight of these breeds have gained popularity in the United States. With the exception of Berkshire, Landrace, Hampshire, and Yorkshire many of the initial breeds in America were developed in the United States in the mid to late nineteenth century. These breeds were developed in response to the surplus grain and consumer demand for fat. Throughout history, swine have been raised for three different purposes, giving rise to lard, bacon, and meat type breeds. These types were developed out of consumer demand, feed availability, and profitability. Today meat type animals are the goal of all producers, but this was not the original purpose of swine breeders. During colonial times, the pig was raised for its lard and producers sought a pig which could deposit ex-

treme amounts of fat. This type persisted into the late nineteenth century. Short stature, early maturity, compact build, and small litter sizes were characteristic of this type, which gained the name cob roller. In 1915, the desired qualities reversed entirely. Breeders demanded a pig of increased body length, which allowed for maximum yield of bacon meat. Bacon type swine were the converse of lard type with their increased length and lean carcass; however, lameness and slow maturity contributed to their failure. Thus, in 1925 the American swine breeders sought to produce animals that were an intermediate between the lard and bacon type animals, the meat hog. The meat type pig combines length of body, muscling, and the ability to quickly reach market weight without excess fat. The producers of today emphasize these traits first and foremost and are usually not tied to a particular breed of swine. However, eight major breeds of pig exist within the United States swine industry and play an important role in production.

■ **Fig. 10.3** Yorkshire. (Courtesy of the National Swine Registry)

■ **Fig. 10.4** Landrace. (Courtesy of the National Swine Registry)

Maternal Breeds

Maternal breeds are typically white in color and excel in litter size, fertility, and milk production. In recent years, improvements in growth rate and carcass quality have been realized. Yorkshires, Landrace, and Chester White are recognized as maternal breeds.

The Yorkshire breed is the leading breed in United State's registries. Yorkshires trace their origins to northern England and in England the Yorkshire breed is known as the Large White. Its first importation into the United States occurred in 1830 when the breed was brought to Ohio. The Yorkshire is always white in color, but may possess black freckles over the body. The ears of this breed are erect and the face is slightly dished. In addition to milk production and large litter sizes, the Yorkshire is known for its durability and soundness. Yorkshires also excel in lean meat production, reduced backfat, and muscular stature.

The Landrace breed was developed in Denmark by crossbreeding native pigs with imported Yorkshire. Denmark held a monopoly on the Landrace breed, granting their export to the United States in 1934, but only permitting their use in crossbreeding. In 1950, Denmark allowed surplus Landrace to be used for pure breeding. American Landrace was subsequently developed from Denmark, Norwegian, and Swedish Landrace. The Landrace is now the fourth most popular breed of swine in the United States. This breed is mainly white although some small black spots are common. The Landrace has ears that droop forward and are known

■ **Fig. 10.5** Chester White. (Image courtesy of Stephen Moeller, The Ohio State University.)

for their body length, muscling in the ham and loin, and their ability to farrow and raise large litters.

The Chester White breed derives from its county of origin, Chester, Pennsylvania. The breed is suggested to have originated from the breeding of various white breed imports from England in the early nineteenth century. These original crossbreeds had reached such uniformity by the mid nineteenth century that they were designated their own breed. Like other maternal breeds, this breed is white and a limited degree of freckling is acceptable. The Chester White are characterized by medium sized drooping ears. This breed is noted for their prolificacy, early maturity, and adaptability. Although its numbers in the United States have dwindled, the breed is seventh in the United States registries.

Paternal Breeds

Paternal breeds of swine are typically colored and excel in leanness, muscling, and increased growth rates. Such breeds include the Duroc, Hampshire, Spotted, and Berkshire.

The Duroc breed was developed in New York and New Jersey in 1812. Interestingly, the breed was named in honor of the founding owner's champion trotting stallion, Duroc. Although originating in New York and New Jersey, most of the breed's development occurred in Ohio, Nebraska, Indiana, Iowa, Kentucky, and Illinois. All Duroc pigs are solid red in color and can range from golden hues to dark mahoganies. The breed has drooping ears and is known for its rapid growth and maturity, heavy muscling in the ham and loin area, and good finishing ability. The Duroc is the second most popular swine breed in the United States registries.

The origin of the Hampshire breed is uncertain. The Hampshire color pattern is similar to the English Saddleback and it is suggested that these belted pigs were imported into the United States in the 1820s to 1830s. The offspring from these animals were sent to Kentucky, which led to further development of the breed, most notably, in Boone County, Kentucky. They are reportedly the original breed selected for use by Smithfield hams in the late 1800s. Hampshire swine are distinguished by their black body and white belt that encompasses the shoulder area and two front and erect ears. The breed is noted for leanness, carcass quality, reduced backfat, and increased loin eye. They are consid-

ered to adapt well to outdoor environments. Today, the Hampshire is the third most popular breed of swine.

The Spotted breed was developed predominantly in Indiana during the mid nineteenth century. The Poland China breed developed in Ohio and the English Gloucester Old Spot breed are the foundations of the Spotted breed. The breed is noted for their rapid growth rates, improved feed efficiencies, and desirable meat qualities. Breed characteristics are similar to Poland China and interestingly, infusion of Poland China into the Spotted breed has been documented into the mid twentieth century. The breed is always spotted in large black and white patterns, with both colors presenting equally.

The Berkshire present in the United States trace their lineage to the founding Berkshire animals of Berkshire and Wiltshire, England. The Berkshire has been an established breed for over two centuries and were first imported into the United States in 1823. The original imports were absorbed into current swine breeds of the United States. Subsequent imports in 1875 were maintained pure and served as the foundation of Berkshires in the United States. The current registry requires that all registrants lineage trace to these imported lines. The Berkshire has erect ears and is black in color with six points of white, including the lower legs, muzzle, and tail. Berkshires produce smaller litters sizes, have lesser growth rates and feed efficiency, and greater fat deposition than other breeds, however, the meat quality is considered exceptional with darker well marbled

■ **Fig. 10.6** Duroc. (Courtesy of the National Swine Registry)

■ **Fig. 10.7** Hampshire. (Courtesy of the National Swine Registry)

pork that is consistently tender and palatable. The darker muscling and excellent quality has led to an increased demand for Berkshire pork, with consumers willing to pay 40–70% more for certified Berkshire pork. Today, the Berkshire is the sixth most popular breed of swine in the United States.

The Poland China breed was produced from foundation stock of Warren and Butler County, Ohio. Breeding of the foundation stock with Russian and Big China breeds led to the development of the Warren County breed. This breed was further improved by breeding with Berkshire and Irish Grazer and in 1872, the breed was established as the Poland China. The Poland China is markedly similar in appearance to that of the Berkshire; however, the Poland China's ears are not erect. The Poland China are exceptional feeders which allow them to be the heaviest of all swine, no matter what age. In addition to its increased rate of gain, this breed is also noted for its prolific litter sizes. The breed produces a carcass of high percent lean and is often selected as a sire breed due to the fact that in crossbred offspring, the dark color of the sire is masked by the white of the maternal breed within the cross which is desirable to packers. The Poland China is the eighth most popular breed of swine.

It should be noted that over 90% of marketed swine are crossbreds. Purebred operations function primarily to provide foundation breeding animals. Purebreds are rarely used in commercial production systems, except in some cases serve as the sire and dam of crossbreeding programs. Prior to 1950, most commercial swine producers of market animals generated breeding stock from their own herds; however, an increasing trend in the industry is the purchase of breeding males and females from specialized breeding suppliers. These suppliers generate and supply purebreds, crossbreds, inbreds, or hybrids that have been developed to emphasize performance and quality.

United States Swine Industry

Swine account for 11.4% of the economic value of the food animal industry with an annual income of $14.2 billion. The United States produces 9% of the world's total pork with only 6.2% of the world's pigs

Fig. 10.9 Berkshire. (Courtesy of Stephen Moeller, The Ohio State University)

Fig. 10.8 Spotted. (Courtesy of Stephen Moeller, The Ohio State University)

Fig. 10.10 Poland China. (Courtesy of Stephen Moeller, The Ohio State University)

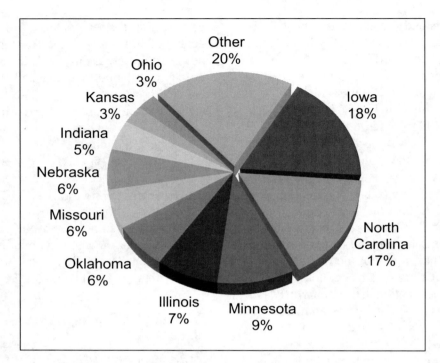

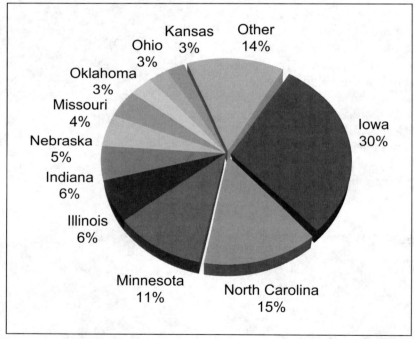

■ **Fig. 10.11** Top ten states in breeding (left) and market (right) swine production during 2008. (USDA, National Agricultural Statistics Service).

and the world demand for pork has allowed the United States pork industry to grow beyond the restraints of domestic demand. Swine are produced in all fifty states; however, the geographical location of dominant swine producing areas parallels the pro-

duction of corn and other small grains in most cases. Proximity to grain production is driven by the fact that feed represents 70% of production costs in swine production. Thus, over 60% of swine are produced in Iowa, Indiana, Illinois, Minnesota,

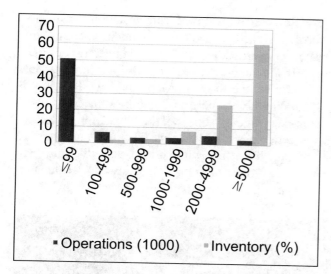

■ Operations (1000)   ▪ Inventory (%)

■ Fig. 10.12 The number of swine operations has decreased nearly 90% in the last three decades, met with an increase in the size of operations. (USDA, National Agricultural Statistics Service).

Nebraska, Kansas, Missouri, and Ohio. These states collectively occupy a region of the United States referred to as the Corn Belt. Interestingly, Iowa has dominated the swine industry since 1880. It should be noted that the second ranked state in swine production, North Carolina, is not a grain producing area. Here, pigs farrowed are transported to the Corn Belt region to be finished. Prior to the 1997 moratorium, which limited the construction of new swine units within the state, North Carolina was the most rapidly expanding swine producing state. The rise of swine production in North Carolina was driven by declining profits from the tobacco and cotton industries as producers sought new avenues of income. The structure of the swine industry in North Carolina is dominated by vertical integration, with a limited number of swine producers controlling the majority of swine produced. The trend of vertical integration in the swine industry has increased over the last fifteen years. The top thirty swine producers owned 15% of sows in production in 1994 and 45% in 2004, with the top three producers alone owning 21%. These corporations, such as Smithfield Foods, own all segments of production including seedstock production, breeding and farrowing, nursery, finishing, and even processing. These segments of production are maintained at different physical locations to minimize the spread of disease. Ownership of all stages in production not only cuts costs, but also allows for greater consistency when producing the market product. As the swine industry becomes increasingly integrated, increasing numbers of pigs are owned by fewer numbers of people. In 1950, 2.2 million swine producers were in operation. This number decreased to 871,200 in 1970 and 87,470 by 2000, equating to approximately a 90% decrease in thirty years. Although the number of operations has declined, the size of these operations has increased. The impact of this trend on the future of the swine industry remains uncertain. As smaller producers view the rise of corporate owned vertically integrated production systems as a threat, proposed legislation has attempted to limit the practices of these corporations and the changing face of the swine industry remains a controversy.

Swine Management Systems

Purebred and Seedstock Production

The first step in developing quality market animals is the establishment of proven lines of maternal and paternal genetics for the inheritance of desirable traits. The swine produced in this stage are selected for their superior genetics and sold to breeding facilities in hopes of passing on these exceptional traits to their offspring. In some cases, the specimens developed may be of outstanding quality and kept by the seedstock producer to collect and distribute the semen or embryos nationally for artificial insemination purposes. Although purebred stock was traditionally used in this stage of the industry, crossbred, hybrid, and inbred seedstock have gained popularity.

Breeding and Farrowing

The animals produced from the seedstock stage are utilized in this segment of the swine industry. Gilts that have not reached sexual maturity may be kept in close proximity to boars to aid in an earlier onset of estrus. Once estrus is reached, the gilts and sows are inseminated using a pen-mating system, hand mating, or artificial insemination. Artificial insemination is the dominant method and is practiced by over 90% of the industry. The successfully inseminated females are either housed in group pens or in individual gestation stalls. Gestation stalls are suggested to reduce physical injury that is incurred by social aggression and reduce early embryonic losses due to physical trauma. However, gestation stalls are currently a focus of ethical debates as these stalls completely confine pregnant swine for the duration of the 114 day gestation. Many of the world's largest swine producers use gestation stalls; however some are banning the use of such stalls due to humane concerns by the public. Florida, Arizona, and Michigan have enacted bans against gestation stalls and Colorado announced their intent to phase out gestation stalls within the next ten years. Following suit, in 2007 Smithfield Foods announced the phase out of gestation stalls and integration of group housing in each of their sow farms in response to consumer pressure.

Sows are transitioned from gestation housing to a farrowing facility prior to the anticipated farrowing date. Sows are individually housed in crates designed to provide the litter access to milk, yet minimize loss of the pigs due to crushing by the sow. It is in this stage that the newborn pigs can be subject to procedures such as castration, tail docking, clipping of needle teeth, and iron injections. The dam and litter are maintained in farrowing crates until the pigs are weaned at fourteen to thirty-five days. Determination of weaning age is dependent on factors including:

■ **Fig. 10.13**   Gestation stalls (left) are at the center of controversy concerning the humane practices of pregnant swine. With planned phase-outs of gestation stall use, methods of group housing (right) are being evaluated. (Courtesy of Stephen Moeller, The Ohio State University)

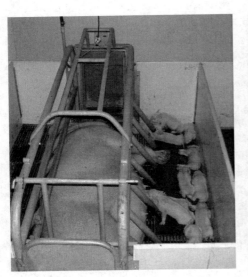

■ **Fig. 10.14**   Farrowing crates (left) house the female and litter from birth until weaning and provide protection for both the growing litter and human handlers Alternatively, farrowing systems may involve pasture based farrowing huts (right) that individually house the sow and litter in outdoor operations. (*Left:* Courtesy of Stephen Moeller, The Ohio State University, *Right:* © Mark William Richardson, 2009. Under license from Shutterstock, Inc.)

disease transmission, rate of pig weight gain, prediction of performance during nursery and finishing stages, subsequent reproductive performance of the sow, and space and inventory considerations. Once weaned, the pigs are transferred to nursery facilities and the sows are reinseminated at estrus.

Nursery and Feeder Pigs

The weaned pigs are grouped according to age, size, and sex and placed into nursery pens. The floors of these pens may be slatted to allow excretory waste to pass through and retain a clean environment. The pigs are fed from a common feed unit a complex, protein rich diet that is highly palatable. It is especially important during this stage to regulate ventilation and temperature to maintain health and ensure optimal growth weights. Once the pigs achieve a weight between thirty-five and fifty pounds, they are moved to the final stage of swine production.

Growing and Finishing

Nursery pigs are moved to a larger housing facility where they are kept and fed until a reasonable market weight is reached, approximately two hundred seventy pounds. The pigs are maintained in groups according to age, size and sex due to the fact that barrows and gilts require different nutritional management for optimal growth. It is especially important during this stage to maintain proper temperature control, particularly during the summer months. Because

■ **Fig. 10.15** Group housing conditions of the grow-finish stage of production. (© Dario Sabljak, 2009. Under license from Shutterstock, Inc.)

pigs lack sweat glands and are unable to perspire, they are especially susceptible to heat stress and can easily become over heated during this stage. Two popular methods exist for cooling the finishing facilities. One system requires the use of large fans which are placed at one end of the barn, opposite to vents that are exposed to the outside. This system draws fresh air through the vents and pulls the expired air into the outside environment. The other method is a fan-less system and necessitates more vents to compensate for the reduced airflow. Often times an entire side of the housing facility is composed of the large vents. During extremely hot periods the swine may be further cooled with watering systems.

Health Management

Swine diseases are difficult and costly to treat and often have lasting effects on the surviving animals. Even completely recovered, animals affected by diseases may never perform efficiently. Biosecurity is a major factor when developing a swine operation. It is a physical impossibility to eliminate all disease causing pathogens; therefore the goal of biosecurity is to prevent new strains of pathogens, those to which the herd has not been exposed, from entering the facility. An effective biosecurity program can result in improved growth and reproductive rates along with a decrease in preweaning mortality. Each of these factors contributes to the overall productivity of the swine operation. Effective biosecurity measures include the physical location of the operation, a minimum distance of 1.5 miles from other swine producing facilities, and proper personnel training that incorporates a work system hierarchy from the highest to the lowest herd health status. For instance, newborn pigs and nursery pigs have the weakest immune systems are susceptible to a greater number of pathogens and are referred to as having a "high health status." The daily chores should start with animals, in the highest health status category. Those animals in the lowest health status category, like the breeding sows, have the strongest immune systems and are likely to have previously come in contact with the pathogens of the farrowing and nursery facilities and should not be affected by any contamination resulting from the previous tasks. However, it is important to properly sanitize before working with the pigs and in between moving from

Fig. 11.10 The trot. Note how the opposite front and rear feet of the horse leave the ground at the same time during the trot. (© Perry Correll, 2009. Under license from Shutterstock, Inc.)

Ponies

Pony breeds are known for their sturdy build and hardiness. Pony breeds of the United States include Shetland, Hackney, Welsh, and Pony of the Americas (POA). The Shetland pony originated in the British Isles and is the smallest of the pony breeds, standing at a maximum of 11.2 hands in height. It is a gentle breed and a popular pony with children. American Shetlands developed in the United States are more refined than the British counterparts originally imported. The Hackney pony originated in England and may reach 14 hands in height. It is routinely used as a trotting and carriage horse. The Welsh pony of Wales also is known for its trotting ability, as well as jumping. The POA were established in the United States in the mid 1950s. Developed from the Appaloosa and Shetland they are a newer breed considered a good riding pony for children. The height may reach 13.2 hands and the breed comes in a variety of coat patterns due to the Appaloosa influence.

Coat Colors

While the color of a horse is not related to performance, color classification is an important tool in horse identification. Furthermore, certain breed registries display a preference for coat color and despite advancements in DNA testing in validation of breed lineage, coat color continues to be used as an indicator of parentage. Nearly all breeds require a description of coat color for registration, thus, it is important to understand and differentiate between coat colors.

Basic Coat Colors and Modifications

There are five basic coat colors recognized in horses: black, brown, bay, chestnut, and white. Horses that are considered black are those which are wholly black, including the hair around the muzzle, eyes, and flanks. True black horses are uncommon and have dark brown eyes, black skin, and a black coat that lacks any permanent reddish or brown sections. However, black horses can possess white markings in which the skin underneath the markings is pink. Foals are not born with a black coat but gradually develop the black coat as they mature. Some black horses will fade to have a smoky appearance, and during the summer months a black horse can be bleached out by the sun's rays but will return to the true black coloring during the winter.

Brown horses may be confused as black, but are distinguished by brown or tan hairs about the muzzle and flank. The mane, tail, and legs are always black. Horses of dark brown are sometimes termed seal brown, whereas light brown horses may be referred to as dark bay.

Bay horses are characterized by a reddish brown body ranging from a light tan-brown to dark shades of mahogany. In order to be classified as a bay, all horses must have black points, which include the mane, tail, tips of the ears, and lower legs. These points, usually on the lower leg, can be covered by white markings and do not alter the horse's classification as a bay. The skin is darkly pigmented except where white markings occur where the skin is pink. Bay is one of the most common coat colors among many horse breeds.

A chestnut horse varies from a light yellowish brown (light chestnut), to a bright and saturated copper (sorrel), to a dark seal brown (liver or black chestnut). The mane and tail of a chestnut horse are usually the same shade as the body; however, when they are a lighter shade of cream, the mane and tail are referred to as flaxen. Darker shades of red or brown are common as well and may appear black, however, black points are never found as the chest-

■ **Fig. 11.12** Shetland (left) and Welsh (right) ponies. (*Left:* © imantsu, 2009. Under license from Shutterstock, Inc. *Right:* © Zuzule, 2009. Under license from Shutterstock, Inc.)

nut is classified by the absence of black hairs. The absence of black hairs on the legs provides further distinction between chestnut and black horses.

White is the rarest coat color in horses. True white horses are born white and remain so throughout their lifetime. White horses are not albino and have completely white hair, pink skin, and usually brown eyes or, less common, blue eyes. The majority of horses that appear white are actually grey horses that become progressively white with age.

Each of the basic color schemes can be modified to yield the coat colors of grey, roan, dilutions, and pinto-paint. Grey coloring is achieved through a combination of white and colored hairs or simply white hairs on darkly pigmented skin. The foal coat of a grey horse is initially solid in color with the addition of increasing white hairs with each coat. Grey horses can be born any of the basic colors, lightening into permanent grey coloring as they mature. Variations occur and can result in flea bitten grey (white coat with red or brown flecks throughout the coat), dapple grey (darker grey coat with light rings of white hair), and rose grey (grey coat with a red-

dish or pink undertone). With regards to skin pigmentation, even if the horse is completely white, it is still considered to be grey if it has black skin. The skin is most easily observable around the eyes and the muzzle.

Roan is a color pattern that results in white hairs becoming intermixed within the basic body color. Often confused with grey, roan horses are born with the same proportion of white hairs that will remain with aging, grey however is progressive. Roan horses generally have solid colored head, neck, and legs. The roan pattern may occur with any background color. White hairs with bay background are considered red roan, white hairs with chestnut are considered to be a strawberry roan, while white hairs with a black background coat results in a blue roan.

Dilutions occur when the intensity of the base color is lessened as an effect of each individual hair. Bay dilutes to buckskin, which are horses tan or golden in color with black points. Duns are very similar to buckskins in that they both have yellow, golden, or sandy body coloring accompanied by black points. However, duns always have unique

Fig. 11.13 Although black is a less common coat color, some breeds of horses, including Friesians, are predominantly black. (© Alexia Khruscheva, 2009. Under license from Shutterstock, Inc.)

Fig. 11.14 One of the most common coat colors among horse breeds is bay, which is characterized by black points including those of the lower legs, mane, and tail. (© Karen Givens, 2009. Under license from Shutterstock, Inc.)

Fig. 11.15 Dapple grey mare and bay foal. Note the white marking on the feet of the bay foal. (© Abramova Kseniya, 2009. Under license from Shutterstock, Inc.)

and distinguishing primitive markings including a dark dorsal strip along the top of the back, a shoulder stripe and sometimes zebra-like striping along the lower legs. As in buckskins, the dun coloring is produced by dilution of bay. Palominos are produced with the dilution of chestnut and produce a horse of golden color that lacks the black points that the buckskin and dun possess. Palominos also have a lighter, flaxen, tail and mane. Double dilution of the chestnut produces the cremello coat color and double dilution of a bay produces a perlino coat color, also a black is diluted by the dun gene to grullo.

Pinto or paint refers to a spotted body with either color on white, or white on color. The spotting is independent of the markings commonly viewed on the head and lower legs of many horses of varying coat colors. The white markings are present at birth and overlie pink skin. Tobiano and Overo are color patterns commonly displayed in paints and pintos. Tobiano horses are characterized by white that crosses the top line. The head is colored, whereas the legs are white (may occur below the knee or hock) and one or both flanks are colored. Conversely, in Overo horses white originates from the belly, but seldom crosses the top line. White spotting is less defined in comparison to the Tobiano and appears splotchy. One or more legs are colored except for white markings.

Coat Color Modifying Genes

The pigmentation of skin and hair is determined by melanin, produced by specialized cells known as melanocytes. In horses there are two types of melanin, one responsible for black/brown pigmentation and the second red/yellow pigmentation. The amount and distribution of melanin is controlled by the presence or absence of alleles that define the common coat colors of the various breeds. Consequently, all horses carry the gene for black or chestnut; however, other genes will modify or mask the expression of the black or chestnut allele. For example, the basic colors of bay and brown are modifications of black. It should be noted that the basic color of white is a consequence of a lack of melanocytes and not a result of modifier genes. The genetic underpinnings of coat color in horses have been a long held interest of breeders. Although considerable progress has been made, color inheritance is complex and a complete understanding of the genetic interplay between alleles responsible continues to evolve.

Extension Gene

The control of black, bay and chestnut resides with the extension gene *E*. This gene controls the extent that black hair is expressed on the body of the horse. The gene extends the amount of melanin responsible for black/brown pigment and reciprocally reduces the melanin responsible for red/yellow pigment. The dominant E allele (EE, Ee) results in a black or bay horse, whereas *ee,* is expressed as

■ **Fig. 11.16**   Buckskin, Dun, and Palomino (clockwise). Note the presence of the dorsal stripe on the Dun and the absence of black points on the Palomino. (*Top:* © Chris Hill, 2009. Under license from Shutterstock, Inc. *Bottom left:* © Stephanie Coffman 2009. Under license from Shutterstock, Inc. *Bottom right:* © mariait, 2009. Under license from Shutterstock, Inc.)

chestnut, a red horse that lacks any black hairs. The E gene is epistatic to the A locus and animals with the dominant *E* will have black hair expressed somewhere on the body, however, the A locus will affect the distribution of black hair.

Agouti Gene

Gene *A* is the Agouti gene and is the determining factor that controls the distribution of black hairs. It is this gene which establishes whether a horse is bay or black. The Agouti coloring is a dominant-recessive trait. Any horse with gene *A* and a gene for black coloring (the presence of at least one gene E) will have black points while the rest of the body remains a shade of red-brown. All bays are consistent with this gene pattern. However, if two recessive Agouti genes are present, *aa*, in combination with at least one gene *E*, then the horse will display black hair over the entirety of its body. Thus, the genotypes AA or Aa restricts black to the points, whereas, the recessive genotype aa results in uniform distribution of black. The horse that does not possess the dominant gene for black hair does not express the Agouti trait phenotypically (a chestnut with the genotype ee); however, the chestnut can pass one of its unexpressed Agouti genes on to its offspring.

Grey

The progressive accumulation of white hairs that contributes to the grey coat is due to the presence of the dominant gene *G* at the grey locus. Grey is epistatic to all other coat color genes and the GG or Gg genotype will produce a grey horse regardless of coat color at birth. Grey horses must have at least one grey parent.

White

True white in horses is due to a single dominant allele, *W*, which does not allow a horse to form pigment in its coat and skin. Gene W is epistatic to all other coat colors; therefore, a horse will still carry the typical genes for coat colors, such as gene *E* or *G*, but will be unable to produce the melanin necessary to express these colors if a dominant gene *W* is present. All white horses are of the genotype Ww as WW is known as a homozygous lethal genotype that results in embryonic death. A homozygous recessive combination, *ww*, allows the horse to be fully pigmented according to the other color genes.

Roan

Roans are considered to contain 50% white hair at birth due to the gene *Rn*. The presence of gene *Rn* allows white hairs to uniformly penetrate the basic coat colors of black, chestnut or bay. Similar to gene W, embryonic lethality is associated with the homozygous dominant genotype *RnRn* and all roan horses are heterozygous.

Tobiano and Overo

The Tobiano pattern is due to the dominant allele *To*. Any horse with the genotype *ToTo* or *Toto* will be Tobiano. The amount of white spotting may be determined by modifier genes at additional loci. Interestingly, the Tobiano gene is absent in the Quarter Horse, Thoroughbred, Standardbred, and Arabian. The Overo pattern is controlled by the Overo allele, *O*. The genotype for Overo horses is Oo, homozygous dominant horses (LWO) are associated with a lethal defect marked by the absence of the colon. Homozygous recessive genotypes (oo) results in the absence of the Overo pattern.

Dilution Genes

Dilutions of basic coat colors of horses have resulted in further variations of possible coat colors. Dilution of coat color is attributed to four distinct genes at different loci. These modifier genes ultimately lighten the base color and are termed diluter genes. Gene *C* is named for cream affects. This gene is expressed in

■ **Fig. 11.17** Tobiano. (© Eric Stacy Bates, 2009. Under license from Shutterstock, Inc.)

an incomplete-dominance pattern. If a horse is genotype CC, its color will be expressed without dilution. However, the genotypic combinations of CC^{cr} and $C^{cr}C^{cr}$ result in a dilution of the base color. If a chestnut horse is heterozygous, CC^{cr}, its red color will be diluted to a yellow, resulting in a palomino; whereas a bay horse will be diluted to buckskin, retaining its black points. Black hairs are generally not affected by the heterozygous form of this gene. A horse of any base color which carries the homozygous combination of $C^{cr}C^{cr}$ will exhibit a greater degree of dilution. All hair colors will be washed to a very pale cream with pink skin and blue eyes resulting in the cremello coloring when the base coat color is chestnut and perlino when the base coat color is bay. The dilution gene D is responsible for dun coloring. Unlike gene C, this gene is expressed in a dominant-recessive pattern. Hence, the homozygous dominant DD does not dilute colorings to the extreme as seen in gene C. Any horse carrying the dominant allele D will express the coloring specific to the dun. The homozygous recessive, dd, has no effect on the original base coloring. A third dilution gene, Z, is responsible for silver dapple coloring. This gene affects only black pigment and is dominant. The presence of this gene dilutes black coat color to brown. The rare pale coat color, mottled skin, and amber eyes of the Tennessee Walking horse is due to dilution by the dominant champagne gene (Ch). Champagne dilution results in a pale brown horse that carries the basic black coat color, yellow horse with brown points with the basic bay color, and a gold horse with yellow points when the horse carries the basic chestnut color.

United States Horse Industry

The United States horse industry has a direct economic impact of $38.8 billion dollars and this value escalates to $102 billion dollars when indirect and induced spending is included. Approximately two million people are reported to own horses, whereas 4.6 million Americans are involved in the equine industry as service providers, employees, and volunteers. These estimates do not include spectators of equine related sporting events. Currently, leading horse states include Texas, California, and Florida.

Although legally classified as a livestock species by legislation, equine use extends beyond agricultural interests. Originally consumed for meat, a commercial market for horse production as a food commodity has never been established in the United States. Since the early 1900s state legislation has restricted the consumption of horse meat in the United States, though peak consumption occurred post World War II. The taboo of eating horse meat is not shared worldwide and several European and Asian countries still permit the marketing of horse meat for consumption. The United States horse industry is diverse and the reasons for keeping horses can be classified into four categories: showing, recreation, racing, and other activities. These other activities can include rodeo, polo, ranch, or police use and breeding. Of these four categories, recreation is the largest segment. Horses are found in all fifty states and are owned by people in all income brackets. Approximately 34% of horse owners have an annual income of less than $50,000 and 28% have an income that exceeds $100,000. The equine industry meets the needs of both rural and urban communities, though the activities and use of horses differ. In rural communities, breeding and training are dominant activities, whereas urban sectors contribute to the use of horses in racing, show, and sale.

Health Management

Horses are subject to a variety of diseases and conditions. Diseases are broadly categorized as infectious when the etiology is parasitic, bacterial, or viral; or non-infectious when the underlying cause is environmental, nutritional, or genetic. Some of the more common diseases include: strangles, colic, and laminitis. Strangles is a highly contagious disease that results from a streptococcus bacterium infection. Although horses of any age may be affected, young horses are more susceptible. The disease is often diagnosed by the presence of abscesses and identification of *Streptococcus equi*. The bacterium is treated with penicillin; however, the introduction of new horses can prolong its occurrence within a herd as the pus from ruptured abscesses can easily contaminate the environment and remains highly infectious for months. Colic is a broad term that refers to the clinical diagnosis of abdominal pain and is a leading cause of death in domesticated horses. Multiple etiologies contribute to the occurrence of colic and include: inflammation of the small intestine, parasitic

Color	Gene	Alleles	Genotypes and Corresponding Phenotypes	
White	White (W)	W	WW:	Lethal
		w	Ww:	Born white. Horse lacks pigment in skin and hair (white)
			ww:	Fully pigmented
Grey	Grey (G)	G	GG:	Born nongrey color but progressively greys as the horse matures. Pigment is present in skin. (grey)
		g	Gg:	Same as GG
			gg:	Does not grey with age. Remains original color
Chestnut	Extension (E)	E	EE:	Has the ability to form black pigment in skin and hair.
		e	Ee:	Same as EE
			ee:	Cannot form black pigment in hair but can in skin
Bay Black	Agouti (A)	A	AA:	Directs black hair to only the points (bay when present with gene E)
		a	Aa:	Same as AA
			aa:	Directs black hair formation over entirety of the body (black when present with gene E)
Palomino Buckskin Cremello Perlino	Cream (C)	C	CC:	Fully pigmented. No dilution occurs
		C^{cr}	CC^{cr}:	Red pigment is diluted to yellow. If black pigment is present, it is unaffected (Chestnut → palomino; Bay → buckskin)
			$C^{cr}C^{cr}$:	Both red and black pigments are diluted to cream. Skin and eye colors also are diluted
Dun	Dun (D)	D	DD:	Dark points are unaffected. Body color is diluted and contain additional dark points including a dorsal strip, shoulder stripe and zebra stripping on the lower legs
		d	Dd:	Same as DD
			dd:	No dilution occurs
Tobiano	Tobiano (TO)	TO	TOTO:	Tobiano spotting pattern
		to	TOto:	Same as TOto
			toto:	No Tobiano pattern present
Overo	Overo (O)	O	OO:	Lethal
		o	Oo:	Overo spotting pattern
			oo:	No Overo pattern present
Roan	Roan (RN)	RN	RNRN:	White hairs are present along with any other body color (roan)
		rn	RNrn:	Same as RNRN
			rnrn:	Lethal

infection and decreased intestinal blood flow, impaction of the digesta (may include feed, sand, or dirt and occurs in the colon), and gaseous distension of the large bowel. A reduction in appetite, decreased fecal output, pawing at the ground, pacing, increased sweating, head tossing, flehman response, repeated lying down and rising, and abdominal distension are all symptoms of colic. Horses in severe discomfort may attempt to roll, which can lead to twisting of the intestines. Treatment may involve walking to relieve intestinal pressure, mineral oil as a laxative to encourage fecal output, or in severe cases, surgery. As parasites are a leading cause of colic, a parasite control program is an important preventative measure

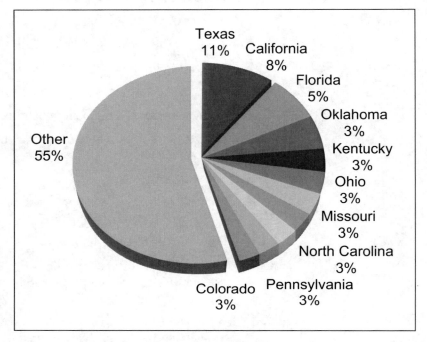

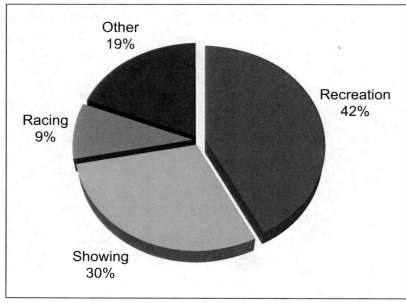

■ **Fig. 11.18** Horse distribution by state (left) and use (right). (American Horse Council, 2005)

against colic. Additionally, maintaining a regular feeding schedule, avoiding sudden changes in diet quality or quantity, and providing access to clean water also reduce the incidence of colic. Lastly, laminitis represents inflammation of the lamina of the inner hoof wall. Often confused with founder, which represents displacement of the coffin bone of the foot, laminitis can occur independently of founder. As with colic, there are multiple etiologies of laminitis and in fact, colic can lead to laminitis in instances where grain is fed in excess. In addition dystocia, repetitive stress to the leg, exhaustion, and infection have been noted as causes underlying laminitis.

Excess grain leads to the over production of lactic acid and promotes endotoxemia, the presence of toxins in the blood as a result of lactic acid damage to the intestinal wall whereas repetitive stress to the leg results in decreased blood flow to the lamina. The condition progresses rapidly and is often observed as a shift in weight onto the heels to alleviate pressure on the toes and increased restlessness and agitation. If not diagnosed within the first few days, the sole of the hoof may bulge downward and founder develops leading to lameness. Without treatment, the coffin bone may rotate downward to perforate the sole. Treatment involves support of the sole, anti-inflammatory medications, hot- and cold-water soaks to encourage circulation to the lamina, and deep bedded stalls to cushion the hoof. With proper diagnosis and treatment the horse often returns to its normal level of activity.

■ **Fig. 11.19** Horses with colic may attempt to roll in an effort to relieve abdominal distension. (© Otmar Smit, 2009. Under license from Shutterstock, Inc.)

Capacity of Production

Mares are seasonally polyestrous, displaying estrus several times annually, but only in response to increasing photoperiod. The mare begins to cycle irregularly at the beginning of the year with regularity in cycles corresponding to peak breeding season of June. As day length shortens in September and October, a return to irregularity in cycling occurs. The occurrences of irregular cycling during the early and later months of the year are associated

■ **Fig. 11.20** Horses with laminitis may shift from a typical standing position (left) to a stretching stance (right) to reduce weight bearing on the hooves. (*Both images:* © Eric Isselée, 2009. Under license from Shutterstock, Inc.)

Fig. 11.21 Newborn foals should stand within two to four hours after birth. (© Melissa Dockstader, 2009. Under license from Shutterstock, Inc.)

with reduced fertility and are known as breeding transition months. As it is responsive to photoperiod, the mare's estrous cycle can be manipulated by the use of artificial lighting to mimic the natural daylight and can be gradually extended to imitate the natural lengthening of the photoperiod in the spring and summer. This allows the mare to ovulate at any wanted time during the year; however, preparation must begin sixty to ninety days before the first ovulation is desired. Manipulation of a mare's estrous is most often used in timing foaling to occur in the first months of the year. This is the ideal timeframe for some breeds as the first of January is the universal birthday for registries, including the Jockey Club. Thus, horses born early in the year have had additional time to grow and develop compared to horses born in the later months of the year. While advantageous to producing a larger foal, reproductive efficiency is sacrificed. For mares cycling regularly, estrus occurs every eighteen to twenty days and lasts three to eight days with ovulation occurring twenty-four to forty-eight hours before the end of estrus. Successful conception can be detected by rectal palpations, ultrasonography, or blood testing for the presence of pregnant mare serum gonadotropin, also known as equine chorionic gonadotropin. The average gestation period of the horse is three hundred forty days, corresponding with spring foaling and an advantageous environment for rapid growth and development of the foal

due in part to the warm weather and availability of new pasture. The mare will often return to estrus within six to twelve days postpartum. This first estrus, known as foal heat, is associated with the uterus returning to a non-pregnant state and conception is unlikely to occur if the mare is bred. Mares should be ideally bred during the second estrus, which is likely to occur approximately thirty days postpartum. Some mares may not display signs of estrus during this period and are said to display a silent heat. Failure to recognize the mare in estrus contributes to national conception rates of 50% to 60% in the equine industry.

Unlike many animal industries, where artificial insemination is used widely, this technology has not been as rapidly adopted by the equine industry due in part to resistance by some breed registries. For example, the Jockey Club, still does not permit horses generated through artificial insemination to be registered as Thoroughbreds. Conversely, the American Quarter Horse registry recognized animals resulting from artificial insemination with fresh, transported or frozen semen. These restrictions have progressively be reduced for many registries over the past 10 to 20 years.

Equitation

The riding and managing of horses is the art of equitation, which there are two primary styles: English and Western. The two styles differ in the methods of mounting, sitting in the saddle, and dismounting. Although there are many similarities in the two riding styles, discrete differences begin with the type of saddle. Western riding combines elements of ranching and the use of horses by cowboys of the West. The saddles used in Western style are large and relatively heavy and have a deeper seat. They are designed to distribute the weight of the rider more evenly over the horse, allow comfort in long distance and rugged travel, and minimize the likelihood of the rider being unseated. Additionally, Western seats are characterized by a prominent pommel and cantle. Horns are also present for securing the lariat, or rope. In contrast, English saddles are distinguished by a flat seat and the absence of prominent pommel and cantle. The use of English seats require greater training to ensure a sure seat, but allows greater communication with

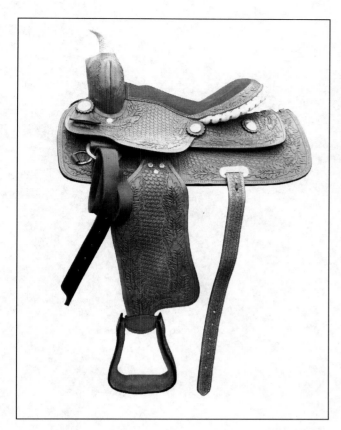

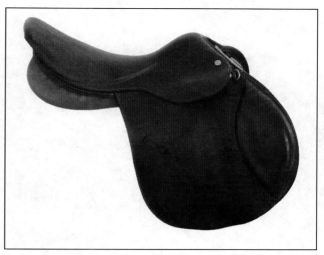

■ **Fig. 11.22** Western (left) and English (right) saddles. (*Left:* © Margo Harrison, 2009. Under license from Shutterstock, Inc. *Right:* © marekuliasz, 2009. Under license from Shutterstock, Inc.)

the horse as the rider sits closer to the horse and is able to communicate more readily with seat and legs. English style allows the horse freedom of movement and is the style used in Olympic equestrian events. With regards to riding, English riders are often required to use both hands on the reigns whereas Western riders only use one hand. The trot or jog also is performed differently between the styles. English riders rise with every other beat during the gait, whereas Western riders sit.

Poultry

"Poultry is for cookery what canvas is for painting . . . It is served to us boiled, roast, hot or cold, whole or in portions, with or without sauce, and always with equal success."
—Jean-Anthelme Brillat-Savarin (1755–1826)

This chapter introduces the segments of the poultry industry, including the primary foundation breeds of poultry that are instrumental in the development of the highly efficient strains used in today's commercial operations. The stages of poultry production for layer and broiler industries are explored, along with health and reproductive management of flocks. Lastly, the nutritional contribution of poultry meat and eggs to the human diet is defined.

Poultry: A Historical Perspective

Origins of the modern domesticated chicken are debated among archeologists and geneticists. Recent mitochondrial DNA analysis provides evidence that a species of wild fowl native to Thailand serves as the maternal ancestor of today's domesticated chicken. The Red Jungle fowl, scientifically known as *Gallus gallus,* still exists undomesticated in the jungles of Thailand and in other parts of Asia. The mitochondrial DNA evidence challenges the previous archaeological estimates of domestication, which dated to 2000 B.C. in India. It now is suggested that the chicken was domesticated twice, 6000 B.C. in Asia and later in northeast India.

The domestication of the chicken in India is coincident with the origins of cockfighting, an ancient and popular sport that was a favored pastime for many civilizations. Cockfighting is considered the catalyst behind the fowls domestication and distribution throughout the world. The sport remains a popular pastime to the majority of the world's population and is often referred to as the world's largest spectator sport. In the United States, the sport is banned in all fifty states with Louisiana imposing the ban in 2008. Poultry also was alluring to individuals not interested in the sport of cockfighting, but intrigued by the rarity of exotic species. During past centuries, it was common to maintain small flocks aboard ships during long voyages at sea. The exotic poultry were frequently transported to and from varying ports because of the traveler's interest; the poultry's relatively small, compact size and ease of maintenance; and provision of food during times of food shortages. Christopher Columbus was the first to introduce chickens to the West during his second voyage in 1493. The formation of the Jamestown Colony in 1607 marked the introduction of the species to the American continent. During this time, it was a common practice for individual families to keep a small flock of chickens that served as a source of both meat and eggs with extra produce being sold or traded. This small-flocking system persisted into the middle of the twentieth century.

The first layer breed, Single Comb White Leghorns, was imported into the United States in 1828. This breed would ultimately become the most important egg-producing breed in the nation. To follow, the first incubator was patented in 1844 and eventually allowed the long-distance shipment of chicks throughout the nation. This development marked the beginning of the commercial hatchery industry, which was later boosted by the United States Postal Service's decision to allow shipment of chicks by mail. In 1918, the United States Department of Agriculture introduced the first federal-state poultry grading standards and programs to implement such grading. The 1920s marked a century that began to

■ **Fig. 12.1** The Red Jungle fowl continues to occupy regions of Thailand and is the ancestor of domesticated chickens. (© Robert J. Beyers II, 2009. Under license from Shutterstock, Inc.)

■ **Fig. 12.2** Cockfighting was a revered pastime of ancient civilizations of the Indus valley, currently occupied by Pakistan. The sport has been banned in all fifty United States following enactment of the ban most recently in Louisiana during 2008. (© Hugo Mases, 2009. Under license from Shutterstock, Inc.)

produce poultry on an industrial scale. The growing industry relied on transportation from the production facilities to areas of consumption and often utilized railroad systems. An outbreak of fowl plague in the New York City railroad yard sparked poultry inspection programs, which lead to the development of the United States Department of Agriculture Poultry Inspection Service in 1926. Three years earlier in 1923, the United States Department of Agriculture announced the first classes, standards, and grades of eggs and these classifications were shortly followed by legal standards and provisions for uniform marketing in 1934. Another significant advancement also was marked by 1923, the development of the electrically heated incubator by Ira Petersime. Subsequent development of the brooder, a device that controls heat and light to warm the chicks from the time of hatching until around five weeks of age, led to virtually all chicks being hatched in incubators by the 1960s.

In the 1920s chicken meat was considered a by-product of egg production and prior to 1940, chicken meat was reserved for special occasions and did not find its destination as an everyday food until mechanization of poultry processing. A mechanical dresser that quickly delivered ready to cook product from live chickens spurred the meat-producing sector of the poultry industry. New developing technologies in the 1960s pertaining to improved diets, equipment, genetics, flock health, and processing reduced the cost of production and prompted the movement of the industry across the Midwest. Shortly after, the poultry industry became vertically integrated as feed producers began raising their own flocks. Today, nearly all of the poultry industry is vertically integrated as the majority of producers are responsible for all stages of production, from the hatchery to processing. It is interesting to note that Colonel Sanders' franchise of Kentucky Fried Chicken, which was initiated in 1956, helped create the commonality of everyday chicken consumption. The introduction of buffalo chicken wings in 1964, the egg McMuffin™ in 1973, and chicken McNuggets™ in 1983 promoted further increases in poultry product consumption. In 1981 the combined cash receipts from the poultry industry bested those of the swine industry, and in 1997 the poultry receipts surpassed those from dairying. Per capita consumption of poultry meat and products is still increasing today, due in large part of the industry's abilities to capitalize on cost effective methods of production and their capability to incorporate and market new and convenient poultry products.

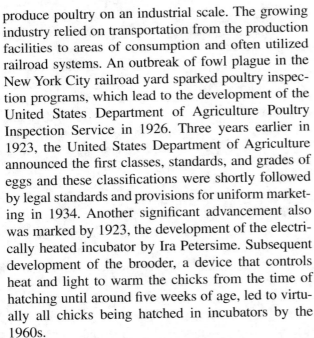

4165. The Dinner Party.

■ **Fig. 12.3**   Poultry initially were raised in small outdoor flocks that provided a source of readily available eggs and meat. This system of poultry production persisted until the mid 1900s. (Library of Congress)

Breeds, Varieties, and Strains of Poultry

The term poultry is applicable to all types of fowl including chickens, turkeys, geese, ducks, pigeons, peafowls, and guineas. Poultry are classified into classes, breeds, varieties, and strains. A class is the broadest form of categorization and refers to a group of birds that has been developed in the same, expansive geographical location. Such classes include American, Asiatic, English, and Mediterranean. A breed is a group of related fowl that when bred, produce consistent traits that are identifiers of its lineage. These traits are usually physical in nature and

include the body shape and type, skin color, and number of toes. Currently, the American Poultry Association recognizes fifty-three large breeds of chicken, eight breeds of turkey, seventeen breeds of duck, and eleven breeds of geese. Varieties are subdivisions of a breed and are based on specific characteristics such as plumage color and comb classification. Strain is the most closely related classification of poultry. A strain indicates a family or breeding population that is more alike than animals within a breed or variety. The term is not associated with purebred lines and is often used to describe the products resulting from a highly systematic inbreeding

■ **Fig. 12.4**   White Leghorn rooster (left) and hen (right) (*Left:* © Elena Butinova, 2009. Under license from Shutterstock, Inc. *Right:* © Wolfgang Zintl, 2009. Under license from Shutterstock, Inc.)

program. The commercial chicken industry of today is primarily based upon the selection of quality and high performing strains of fowl that are bred to excel in essential factors important to each industry. For the egg production systems, these include the number of eggs and their size, eggshell quality, and fertility. For broiler, or meat, production these traits are white plumage, egg production, fertility, hatchability, growth rate, and carcass quality. Turkeys, ducks, geese, and other poultry industries rely primarily on pure breeds of fowl when marketing their products.

Unlike other livestock industries, no individual registries exist for recognizing specific poultry breeds. Instead, the American Poultry Association functions as a comprehensive breed registry and maintains a standard for all three hundred fifty recognized breeds and varieties of chickens, bantams, ducks, geese, and turkeys in its *American Standard of Perfection* publication. This publication illustrates the size, shape, color, and various other physical features that describe each standard breed.

Layer Breeds

Commercial egg-producing flocks in the United States trace to the Single Comb White Leghorn, which was imported into the United Stated in 1823. These are the most popular breed of chicken in the United States today and are used solely for the production of eggs. Leghorns and their strains are characterized by yellow skin color, which is especially apparent on the legs and beak. The pigmentation is a consequence of ingested xanthophyll*s* from the diet and is associated with stage of production. As stage of production increases the xanthophylls from the skin are deposited in the egg yolks and the skin becomes bleached. Increased yellow pigmentation is associated with birds that have laid relatively few eggs, whereas, decreased pigmentation is indicative of birds that have laid many eggs over the productive life.

The Rhode Island Red is a dual purpose breed developed in New England in the mid nineteenth century. Although relatively limited numbers of purebred Rhode Island Reds are used in commercial production, they serve as the foundation breed for the brown egg laying strains used today. The breed is suggested to trace its origins to the red Malay breed of Asia. Because of their dual purpose utilization, producing quality eggs and meat, this breed is recommended for small outdoor flocks. With feed production costs of the Rhode Island Red being greater than the White Leg horn, egg costs for brown eggs exceed the costs for white eggs.

Broiler Breeds

The broiler industry of the United States has relied on the development of chickens that attain market weight of four pounds by six to seven weeks of age and traces its origins to the Plymouth Rock and Cornish breeds. Plymouth Rock was developed in the United States during the mid nineteenth century and is used predominantly as the maternal parent line. The broiler industry of the 1920s began with

■ **Fig. 12.5** Rhode Island Red rooster (left) and hen (right). (*Left:* © Ant Clausen, 2009. Under license from Shutterstock, Inc. *Right:* © Brasiliao, 2009. Under license from Shutterstock, Inc.)

the use of the Barred Plymouth Rock, currently strains developed from the White Plymouth Rock dominate the specialized broiler industry. In general, white varieties of poultry are preferred due to the absence of dark pin feathers, feathers just emerging through the skin. These feathers are not easily removed during the processing of the carcass and if noticed, can detract from the value of the carcass. For this reason, white pinfeathers are preferred because of their likelihood of remaining undetected. The paternal parent line is represented by the Cornish breed. Developed in England for muscling and conformation, fertility is reduced in the Cornish breed. Similar to the layer industry, the meat industry is dominated by the development of strains and purebred chickens are no longer commercially used by the industry.

■ **Fig. 12.6** Barred Plymouth Rock. (© liubomir, 2009. Under license from Shutterstock, Inc.)

Turkey Industry Breeds

The American Poultry Association lists eight breeds of turkey: Bronze, Beltsville Small White, Narragansett, Black, Slate, Bourbon Red, White Holland, and Royal Palm. Turkeys are native to North America and were domesticated within the last five centuries. With the exception of the White Holland, recognized turkey breeds were developed in the United States. Of commercial importance is the Broad-Breasted White, a strain developed in the 1950s from the crossbreeding of the Bronze and White Holland breeds. The Broad-Breasted turkeys were developed for increased breast muscle and as a consequence artificial insemination is required for mating.

Duck and Geese Breeds

Domestic ducks originate from the Mallard duck and are considered one of the most versatile of poultry, able to adapt to a wide range of climatic conditions and unsusceptible to diseases of other poultry including Marek's disease. Duck breeds are classified as meat or egg producers. The breeds of ducks most utilized for meat production include the White Pekin, Aylesbury, and Muscovy. The White Pekin breed originated in China and was introduced to the United States in 1870s. It is considered the most popular breed of duck raised in the United

States because of its excellence market carcass achieved at seven to eight weeks of age. White Pekins do not usually possess maternal qualities and will rarely raise a brood. Today, this breed is highly recognizable to the general public due to its long running use in the Aflac insurance commercials. The most productive of the egg-laying breeds of duck are the Khaki Campbell and Indian Runner, first and second in production, respectively. The Khaki Campbell originated in England and although uncommon, production rates of 365 eggs per duck per year have been reported. The Indian Runner duck originated in present day Indonesia and was developed into an egg producing breed in Western Europe.

Domestic geese were domesticated from different species of waterfowl in different geographical locations. The Greylag goose is the wild ancestor of American and European domestic geese, while Asian and African breeds descend from the swan goose. Domestication traces to five thousand years ago. There are eleven breeds of geese recognized by the American Poultry Association: Toulouse, Embden, African, Sebastopol, Pilgrim, American Buff, Saddleback Pomeranian, Chinese, Tufted Roman, Canada, and Egyptian. The Embden, Toulouse, and African are the most popular geese breeds in the United States. The Embden was one of the first breeds imported into the United States and originated from Germany. It is characterized by rapid growth and early maturity. The Toulouse originates from France and is one of the largest of the breeds. Its large appearance is further heightened by its loose feathering. The African is distinguished by the protuberance on its head. It is noted for its rapid growth rate and early maturity, however, its com-

■ **Fig. 12.7** Royal Palm, Bronze, and Broad-Breasted White turkeys (clockwise). (*Top:* © 2009. Under license from Shutterstock, Inc. *Bottom left:* © Babusi Octavian Florentin, 2009. Under license from Shutterstock, Inc. *Bottom right:* © Joy Brown, 2009. Under license from Shutterstock, Inc.)

mercial use is limited by the presence of dark pin-feathers. In addition to their use as a food commodity, geese are used for eggs, show, and as guard animals.

Ratites

Emus and ostriches are flightless birds that originate from Australia and Africa, respectively, and were domesticated within the last two centuries. Commercial ostrich and emu production in the United States is limited, but increasing. Lack of knowledge of ratite nutrition, disease prevention, and optimal environmental conditions has contributed to their limited use. Original uses of the birds included processing for the hide, feathers, and oil; the meat was considered a by-product. Marketing ratite meat as a meat of

similar quality to lean beef, with reduced calories in comparison to chicken and turkey has promoted the ratite industry.

United States Poultry Industry

The per capita consumption of broiler meat has increased steadily since the 1960s, contributing to a threefold increase that equates to an average annual consumption of sixty pounds per person. Per capita consumption of turkey is approximately fourteen pounds, whereas annual consumption of duck is less than 0.4 pounds. Per capita egg consumption was the greatest in the United States during 1945 with an average of four hundred three eggs eaten per person

■ **Fig. 12.8** Pekin, Indian Runner, and Muscovy ducks (clockwise). (*Top:* © Alistair Scott, 2009. Under license from Shutterstock, Inc. *Bottom left:* © Istomina, 2009. Under license from Shutterstock, Inc. *Bottom right:* © Sally Wallis, 2009. Under license from Shutterstock, Inc.)

■ **Fig. 12.9** Embden, Toulouse, and African geese (clockwise). (*Top left:* © Andy An, 2009. Under license from Shutterstock, Inc. *Top right:* © lynnlin, 2009. Under license from Shutterstock, Inc. *Bottom:* © 2009. Under license from Shutterstock, Inc.)

per year. Per capita egg consumption has been variable with a general trend toward decreased consumption. The decline in egg consumption is attributed to concerns over cholesterol intake and a lack of ready to eat packaged products. Per capita egg consumption today is around two hundred fifty-five eggs, with over one third of the eggs produced being consumed by the Hispanic population.

The value of the poultry industry, estimated from the sales of broilers, eggs, and turkeys, is estimated at $31.9 billion; $21.5 billion attributed to broilers and $6.68 billion attributed to eggs. The poultry industries in the United States have evolved from multiple small flocks owned by multiple individuals, to a limited number of large, consolidated production systems. The majority of the broiler, turkey, and egg industries are vertically integrated, with over one half of the egg producing industries experiencing this formation as well. Consolidation of the broiler industry began in the mid 1900s and has served as the catalyst for consolidation of other

segments of the poultry industry. As encountered with other livestock industries, broiler operations have been decreasing in number, but increasing in the number of birds kept on the remaining farms. Broiler chicks placed on feed by companies may exceed one hundred seventy million birds weekly, with nine billion marketed annually. The majority of the broiler industry is located in the southern and southeastern states because of the climate, which reduces housing costs, labor costs, and provides nearby populations which act as markets for the meat products. The top producing broiler states include Georgia, Arkansas, Alabama, North Carolina, Mississippi, Texas, South Carolina, Delaware, and Virginia. The egg industry averages three hundred forty-five million laying birds and produces ninety-one billion eggs annually. In the 1980s egg production increased due to an increase in number of eggs laid annually by hens, with an approximate increase of one egg per hen per year. The top producing egg states include Iowa, Ohio, Pennsylvania, Indiana,

■ **Fig. 12.10** Emu (left) and ostrich (right). (*Left:* © Arvind Balaraman, 2009. Under license from Shutterstock, Inc. *Right:* © Natalia Yudenich, 2009. Under license from Shutterstock, Inc.)

Texas, California, Georgia, Arkansas, Nebraska, Minnesota, Florida, and North Carolina.

The turkey industry has experienced growth and consolidation akin to that of the broiler and egg industries, but to a lesser degree. Approximately two hundred sixty million turkeys are produced annually in the United States, which corresponds to seven billion pounds of turkey meat. An average of 70% of this meat is marketed as processed products as opposed to sold whole. The turkey industry is not geographically concentrated. North Carolina and Minnesota are the leaders in turkey production and are followed by Arkansas, Virginia, Missouri, and Pennsylvania. Turkey production has increased over the years due in large part to the increasing population, exports, and the marketing of turkey outside of the traditional holiday fare.

In 2007, there were over thirty-one thousand farms producing ducks with 3.9 million sold. Geese farms totaled almost nineteen thousand with 177,812 birds sold. Ducks are marketed as broiler, roaster, or mature ducks and geese are marketed as young or mature. Marketing is based on age and weight, with mature birds representing layer and breeder birds past production and the meat used in

processed products. The duck industry is focused in Indiana and Wisconsin, whereas the geese industry is predominant in California and South Dakota.

The ratite industry is limited, but expanding within the United States. As of 2006, there were one thousand Ostrich producers raising approximately one hundred thousand birds; however, number of ostriches sold was approximately eleven thousand. Emu production has expanded to forty-three states. Approximately one million emus are owned by ten thousand producers, the greatest numbers are located in Texas. In 2007, 28,443 emus were sold. Effective 2002, meat from ostrich and emu became subject to mandatory United States Department of Agriculture inspection. Sold as a specialty item in restaurants with limited availability retail, the price of ostrich and emu exceeds that of beef, pork, chicken, and turkey.

Poultry Management Systems

Vertical integration of the poultry industry has led to specialized production segments within the layer and broiler industries including breeding flocks, hatchery, grow-out operations, and market egg pro-

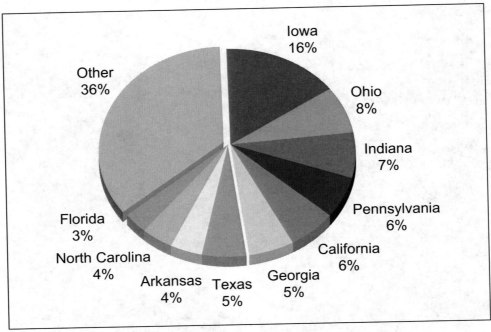

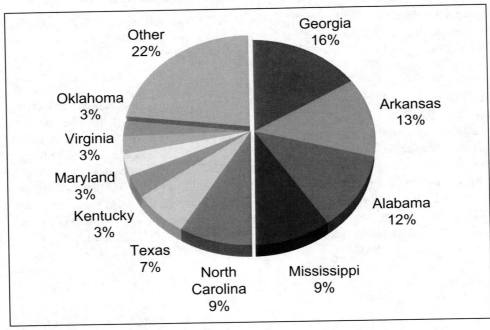

■ **Fig. 12.11**   Layer (top) and broiler (bottom) distribution by state during 2008.
(USDA, National Agricultural Statistics Service)

ducing operations. Breeding flocks provide the eggs to supply broiler and layer industry demands for production birds, eggs produced by breeder flocks are incubated and hatched at the hatchery, hatched chicks enter grow-out operations and provide birds for the breeder flock, broiler, or layer segments.

Incubation and Hatching

Incubation is the act of bringing an egg to hatch. With many poultry, artificial methods of incubation support the hatch of a fertilized egg independent of the hen. Poultry are oviparous and development of the young occurs outside the uterus. Structural de-

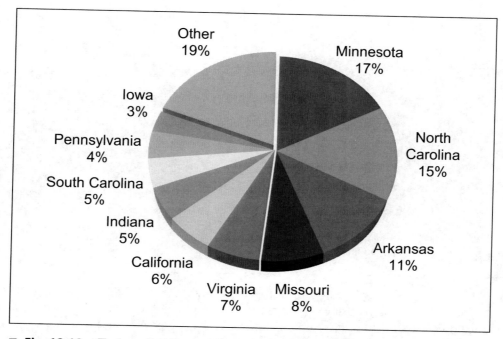

■ **Fig. 12.12** Turkey distribution by state during 2008. (USDA, National Agricultural Statistics Service)

velopment occurs soon after fertilization and continues through incubation. Before the egg is laid cells begin to acquire specialized function that is central to embryonic development. Within the first twenty-four hours of incubation, the nervous, digestive, and visual systems of the chick embryo begin to appear. By the end of day two, the heart begins to beat. At day nine, the embryo acquires a birdlike appearance, coincident with the initiation of beak development. The protein rich albumin is completely depleted and the yolk is the main energy source for the embryo once day sixteen is reached. Day nineteen signals the remaining yolk and sac to enter the body of the embryo through the umbilicus, which will allow early survival until a post-hatch food source is identified. The embryo officially becomes a chick on day twenty and hatching follows on day twenty-one.

Poultry differ in incubation periods and it is crucial when raising poultry to be knowledgeable about the individual breeds in order to raise successful broods. A central aspect to successful incubation is maintaining a uniform and correct environment. Forced-air, or fan, incubators are the most commonly utilized incubation system in the commercial industry. The incubators control temperature and

Reproduction in Poultry

Species	Incubation (days)	Eggs/Year
Chicken (layer type)	21	240
Chicken (broiler type)	21	170
Turkey	28	105
Goose	28-32	15-60
Duck (Pekin)	28	110-175
Emu	57-62	25
Ostrich	42	50

humidity, rotate the eggs, and facilitate an adequate supply of fresh air. The sizes of the incubators can vary and range from one hundred egg capacity to one hundred thousand eggs or more. Provided adequate techniques are used, hatchability of artificially

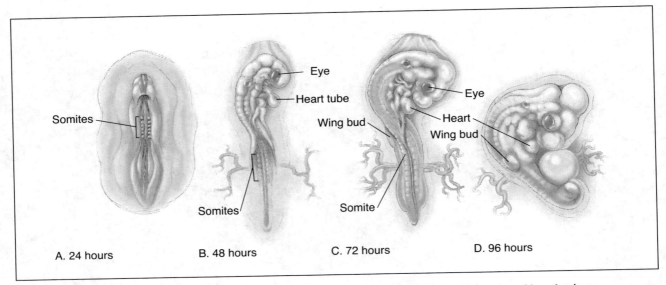

Somites

Eye
Heart tube
Somites

Eye
Wing bud
Heart
Wing bud
Somite

A. 24 hours   B. 48 hours   C. 72 hours   D. 96 hours

■ **Fig. 12.13** The chick embryo grows and develops rapidly and within three weeks of incubation emerges as a fully formed chick. During the first day of embryonic development the nervous, digestive, and visual systems begin to develop. By day three, discernible features of the chicken appear, including the wing buds. The somites will differentiate into skeletal muscle and skin with further development. (© Kendall Hunt Publishing Company)

incubated eggs may exceed 90% for chickens, although hatchability estimates of 65–70% may be more common for geese and ducks.

Temperature is arguably the most critical requirement for successful incubation and hatching. When an egg is laid the drop in external temperature relative to the internal temperature of the hen arrests embryonic development. The egg may be held at a temperature of 65° F for seven days before beginning incubation, which will reinitiate embryonic development. While this may reduce hatchability, it allows for eggs that were laid at different times to hatch within a narrow window of time. For chickens, 99 to 103° F is an optimal beginning temperature range for chickens. At the end of the fourth day of incubation, the temperature should be lowered by 0.25 to 0.5° F. Three days before hatching, the temperature should be lowered a second time by 1.0 to 1.5° F. This last, and fairly dramatic, change in temperature is due to the chick's transition from embryonic respiration to aerobic respiration. Aerobic respiration produces increased heat, raising the overall temperature of the incubator. Greater than optimal temperatures may accelerate embryonic development, increasing the risk of mortality and malforma-

tion of chicks. Lower than optimal temperatures retards the embryonic process and also increases the risk of mortality and deformation.

The optimal humidity maintained by incubators can range anywhere from 60% to 70% depending on the stage of incubation. The later phases require more humidity for the upcoming hatching of the chicks. Humidity is important in order to avoid evaporation of water from the egg. Rotation of the eggs also is a critical aspect of incubation. If not frequently rotated, the embryo may become fixed to the shell membrane and further development will be impaired. The timing and control of egg rotation is mechanized on all modern, commercial incubators. Maximum hatchability is achieved when the egg is rotated five or more times daily. However, during the three days preceding hatching, the egg should not be turned. At this late stage, the embryos are moving into the ideal position for hatching and are not benefited by egg rotation.

Proper ventilation is necessary to maintain appropriate oxygen and carbon dioxide concentrations. The oxygen content should be 21%, while the carbon dioxide accumulation should never exceed 0.5%. During the incubation stage, the eggs are can-

males give birth standing and parturition typically occurs within the morning hours. In her native environment, birth during early daylight hours allows the cria to dry, stand, and nurse before the onset of the cooler night time temperatures of the higher altitudes, which contributes to a greater chance of survival for the offspring. Females also are reported to delay birth under unfavorable conditions. Singleton births are common, whereas twinning is rare, occurring only once in every two thousand live births.

Llamas as a Food Commodity

Although not consumed in the United States, llama meat is an important commodity in other countries. In Bolivia, llama meat consumption increased 76% between 1985 and 2004. Studies have shown that llama meat is a high protein, reduced fat, reduced cholesterol alternative to other red meats consumed, including beef and sheep. Furthermore, 42% of fatty acids are found as monounsaturated fatty acids and 7% as polyunsaturated fatty acids. Llama milk has reduced calories and fat compared to cow milk and increased concentrations of lactose. Although protein concentrations between cow and llama milk are similar, the latter does not contain detectable concentrations of β-lactoglobulin. The apparent lack of β-lactoglobulin makes llama milk an attractive alternative to cow milk for humans suffering from milk allergens as this protein is suggested to play a role in the allergen response. Furthermore, llama milk is greater in calcium with reduced concentrations of sodium when compared to cow milk. Despite the benefits of llama meat and milk, the current United States industry does not permit affordable production of either of these commodities.

■ **Fig. 13.9** Crias remain with the female until weaning at six to eight months of age. (© nousefor-name, 2009. Under license from Shutterstock, Inc.)

■ **Fig. 13.10** A Bolivian couple prepares to slaughter a llama in order to sell the meat and skin. (© Carlos Cazalis/Corbis.)

Aquaculture

"Give a man a fish, you feed him for a day. Teach a man to fish, you feed him for a lifetime."

—*Chinese Proverb*

This chapter introduces aquaculture, the farming of organisms in controlled aquatic environments. The aquaculture industry in the United States is discussed along with the rudimentary production techniques for rearing aquatic organisms in fresh water and marine environments. Prominent species produced in the United States and their specific managerial requirements are highlighted. Lastly, the current challenges experienced by the industry and the nutritional benefits of fish are explored.

Aquaculture: A Historical Perspective

The cultivation of aquatic organisms under controlled or semi-controlled conditions has been practiced for centuries. Historians have traced its roots to Egypt with the culture of Tilapia and China with the culture of carp occurring as early as 2000 B.C. in both regions. The Chinese are responsible for the first detailed writings of fish culture in a book titled *The Classic of Fish Culture* (500 B.C.). It offered the first written description of pond structure and method of propagation of common carp. Oyster farming by the Japanese and Romans trace to 100 B.C. and for many societies aquaculture was considered an extension of the agriculture practiced on land. Ancient forms of aquaculture involved harvesting of immature fish and shellfish from marine environments and continued rearing in confined systems. The first modern form of aquaculture began in 1733 when a German farmer collected, fertilized, and grew-out hatched fish; however, the commercial practice of aquaculture would remain obscure until the 1960s.

As early as the 1870s, some aquatic animal populations were already in decline in the United States. The United States Fish and Fisheries Commission was established in order to combat this issue by developing technology to mass produce, transport, and stock marine and freshwater fish and shellfish. Subsequently, the interest and expansion of recreational fishing in the United States led to the creation of hatcheries that were responsible for stocking, or introducing, fish into lakes, rivers, or ponds of establish or enlarge the population. Post War World II, the commercial bait industry was established and by the 1950s the catfish industry began to take root. Important aspects relative to the aquaculture industry had not been defined at this point in time, including a fundamental understanding of feeds, diseases, and water quality requirements and it was not until the late nineteenth century that a scientific approach was brought to the field.

Early attempts of aquatic farming often failed as operators were inexperienced in fish culture, ponds were not properly built, low-value species were being raised, and there was limited technical support for the industry. This was to change in the 1970s, which was marked as an era of great advancement in aquaculture as government laboratories and universities became interested in and initiated efforts to understand management, nutrition, genetics, reproduction, and disease. Aquaculture is considered the fastest growing sector of the food industries, increasing 10% per year and accounting for more than 30% of all fish consumed. In the last three decades the importance of aquaculture as an economic sector in United States agriculture has been realized; however, the United States produces only 3% of total world aquaculture products.

The Aquaculture Industry

Aquaculture is a means of farming aquatic organisms including fish, reptiles, and aquatic plants. Successful cultivations are underway in fresh water, brackish water, and salt water. The aquaculture industry in the United States was first created as a way of combating the decline in native fish populations and has been used to augment recreational fishing. In recent decades, it has evolved into an important food supplier to the nation and continues to grow with the increased demand for seafood, concern over the shortage in trade of fishery products, and static commercial harvest of wild fish. Although per capita consumption of seafood in the United States has remained static at sixteen pounds per year, increased knowledge of the relationship between diet and health is anticipated to lead to increased consumption in future years and global seafood demand is expected to increase 70% during the next thirty years. The United States is the second leading nation in seafood imports and currently imports 45% of the total seafood consumed. Tilapia, Atlantic salmon, and shrimp remain the greatest imports and growth in shipments of these products to the United States increased 291%, 50%, and 42%, respectively, between 2000 and 2006. The combined value of these imports was $5.9 billion in 2006. It is suggested that by 2020 aquaculture will provide the total supply of these seafoods consumed in the United States. The United States, like all nations is unable to increase their wild harvest fishing industry. Worldwide harvests of nearly two hundred twenty-one thousand pounds of seafood have not changed since 1989. Decades of unsustainable fishing and pollution has contributed to 70% of aquatic species being fully exploited, overexploited, depleted, or recovering from depletion.

The United States Department of Agriculture Census of Agriculture in 2005 indicated that the aquaculture industry in the United States contributed over

■ **Fig. 14.1** Dam construction for a fish rearing pond, 1936, Michigan. (Library of Congress)

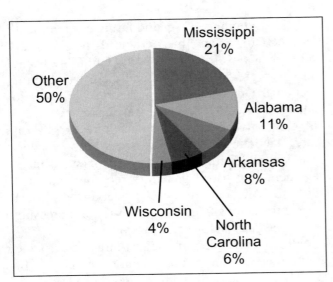

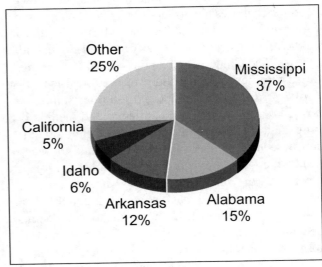

■ **Fig. 14.2** Food fish farm distribution (left) and sales (right) by state during 2005. (USDA, National Agricultural Statistics Service)

1.1 billion dollars to the economy with 61% attributed to the production of food fish. Also denoted in this survey, the top aquaculture states included Mississippi, Arkansas, Alabama, Louisiana, and Washington. The production of catfish, trout, salmon, tilapia, shrimp, mussels, clams, oysters, hybrid striped bass, crayfish, ornamental fish, and other fish species as well as plants contribute an estimated one hundred eighty-one thousand jobs from the reported 4300 aquaculture farms. Although the United States is considered the fourth leading nation in aquaculture contributions to the world market, the United States is only accountable for 2.7% of total world production. China is the leading nation in aquaculture production holding 23% of production; other leading nations include Peru (3%) and India (2.9%).

Aquaculture Production Methods

Management techniques in aquaculture vary in labor intensity and those who participate in this industry range from the backyard hobbyists to the producer whose income rests with the success of the farm. When done properly, raising fish can be very efficient. Fish require less space in relation to land surface area because fish farms consist of three-dimensional rearing systems with the added dimension of depth in which to grow. Because fish are cold blooded and expend less energy on maintaining body temperature, fish are the most efficient at converting feed to flesh, even more so than poultry. This contributes to their high feed to gain ratio. Even the feed that the fish eat lend to their efficiency as they are capable of utilizing wastes and waste by-products. In addition, fish have greater flesh to bone ratio than do land livestock. Accordingly, there are advantages of aquaculture production over land based agriculture; however, the industry lags behind land based agriculture technologically, which limits its expansion. The range and methods of aquaculture production greatly

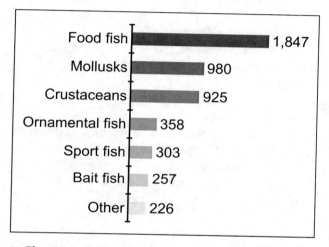

■ **Fig. 14.3** United States aquaculture farm type and number during 2005. (USDA, National Agricultural Statistics Service)

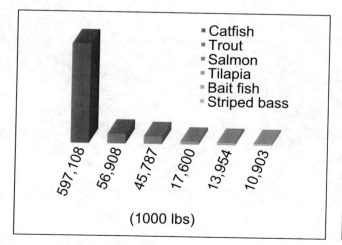
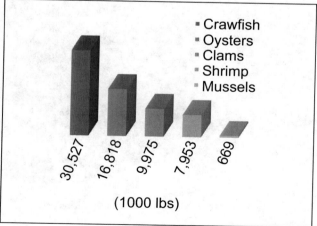

■ **Fig. 14.4** United States production of food fish (left) and shellfish (right) during 2005. (USDA, National Agricultural Statistics Service)

varies according to environmental and social conditions and is greatly dependent upon the species raised. For these reasons, aquaculture has been molded into an exceptionally diverse enterprise and continues to be developed according to emerging discoveries. Although improvements in aquaculture are needed, there are some underlying commonalities in the production and management of aquaculture that has contributed to its current success. Fish and plants can be produced by utilizing naturally occurring water features or by artificially creating water reserves. These man-made structures can be earthen or concrete. In a natural freshwater or marine setting, fish pens, nets, or cages can be used as a means of raising and harvesting organisms. Depending upon the species and available resources, certain management systems are better suited to the environment.

Ponds

Ponds are the most prevalent method of production, particularly in the United States, and are the primary method of catfish production. Ponds may consist of spawning, fingerling, and finishing. Site location is important to ensure adequate fresh water, protection from flooding, and ease of drainage. Most ponds are rectangular in shape to facilitate feeding ease and harvest. Pond size of fifteen to twenty acres is common with depth ranging from three to six feet.

Flow through Raceways

Raceways consist of a series of long, narrow channels through which there is continuous flow of fresh, oxygenated water. Trout are routinely produced using this system. Dimensions of raceways vary, but often retain a 30:3:1 ratio for length:width:depth. Raceways are constructed with an 8% to 10% slope to accommodate gravity driven water movement. The continuous movement of water provides aeration and removes waste. Facility cost of raceways is increased compared to other systems; however, these costs are reduced when water movement is supported by gravity and does not require manual pumping. Raceways may be constructed in conjunction with water recirculating systems in which water that has passed through the system is pumped to a processing facility that removes waste so that the water may be reused.

Recirculation Tanks

Recirculation tanks are a more recently introduced method of aquaculture production. The system consists of a biological filter, solid waste filter, pump, and tank. The method recirculates 90% of the water contained within a closed loop system. Water that circulates through the system undergoes mechanical filtration of the solid waste and subsequent biological filtration for removal of metabolic gasses, am-

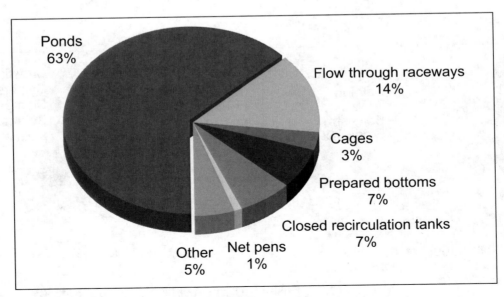

■ **Fig. 14.5**   Leading methods of aquaculture production.

monia, and nitrates before being reintroduced to the production tank. Recirculation tanks are confined to indoor systems and as water temperatures can be monitored and adjusted to the needs of fish, the system is not influenced by fluctuating environmental temperatures. The system also offers improved disease and predator control; however, high-capital investment, increased maintenance costs, and increased management limit their current use.

■ **Fig. 14.6** Ponds for catfish production in Mississippi. (© Jim Wark/AgStock Images/Corbis)

Net Pens

Net pens involve the suspension of nets, or cages, in existing water resources. The system is routinely used in marine culture of salmon and the freshwater culture of crustaceans. Water exchanges freely through the system; however, as stocking density is increased, the incidence of disease is increased. Furthermore, free exchange of water and waste from the system to the natural environment has raised concern over the ecological impacts of these commercial systems. In comparison to ponds and raceways, start-up costs are reduced as existing water resources are utilized.

Aquaculture Systems

Catfish

There are thirty-seven species of North American catfish; however, only seven species are suitable for commercial production including blue, white, black bullhead, brown bullhead, yellow bullhead, and flathead. Catfish production is the largest segment of the United States aquaculture industry and is accountable for 42% of aquacultures total economic value and 69% of the economic value of food fish. Efficient growth of catfish is dependent on water temperatures and optimal at temperatures that average 85° F. Metabolic rate, and therefore appetite and feed consumption, is reduced when water temperatures are decreased. At temperatures of 45° F an ad-

■ **Fig. 14.7** Raceways used in trout culture. (*Both images:* © liseykina, 2009. Under license from Shutterstock, Inc.)

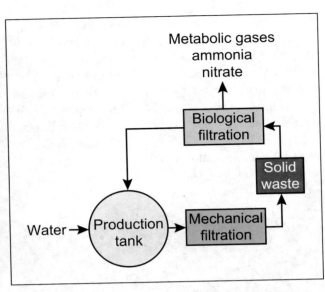

■ **Fig. 14.8**   Recirculation tanks (left) use a closed loop system of filtration (right) for recirculation of existing water. (*Left:* © Jan Kaliciak, 2009. Under license from Shutterstock, Inc.)

■ **Fig. 14.9**   Net pens are used in the culture of salmon and rely on existing water resources. (*Left:* © Konstantin Karchevskiy, 2009. Under license from Shutterstock, Inc. *Right:* © Kheng Guan Toh, 2009. Under license from Shutterstock, Inc.)

ditional three to six months of growing time is required for catfish produced in northern regions of the United States. For this reason, production of catfish is mainly contained to Alabama, Arkansas, Louisiana, and Mississippi. Currently, Mississippi produces over half of all catfish grown in the United States and greatly contributes to the United States claim of the world's largest catfish producer. Catfish are harvested at one to one and one half pounds in weight at a targeted age of eighteen months. Growth rates are increased in commercially raised fish in comparison to fish harvested from natural waters, which reach an average weight of one pound by twenty-four months of age.

The type of feed is especially important in catfish production and contributes to increased growth rates of commercial fish. Feed is available in many variations and is classified by sinking, slow sinking, or floating. A primary factor in determining which feed is the most suitable is water temperature. Ideally, a floating feed is most desired because it allows the producer to observe feeding rates and pat-

■ **Fig. 14.10** Brown Bullhead catfish. (© David Dohnal, 2009. Under license from Shutterstock, Inc.)

■ **Fig. 14.11** Rainbow trout. (© Evok20, 2009. Under license from Shutterstock, Inc.)

■ **Fig. 14.12** Tilapia. (© Olga Lyubkina, 2009. Under license from Shutterstock, Inc.)

terns. However, floating feed is expensive and can only be utilized in waters that are above 65° F. If the water is below this temperature, the catfish remain in the deeper depths of water and sinking or slow sinking feeds must be used. In order to reduce costs, most producers feed only once per day, usually in the morning. However, feeding schedules vary depending upon the season as some producers may choose to convert to every other day feedings in the fall and spring. A mechanical blower is usually employed to disperse the feed widely across the entire water surface to maximize the feeding opportunity.

Trout

Raising trout is the oldest form of aquaculture in the United States and dates to the 1800s. Trout contributes 7% of aquacultures total economic value and 12% of the economic value of food fish. Trout farming was originally developed as a way of supplementing the natural streams, lakes, and rivers with a greater population of recreational fish. Rainbow trout are the most popular raised species with Brook and Brown trout also being raised. Twenty states are significantly involved in trout production; however, Idaho is the most prominent trout producing state because of its natural springs and accounts for over 50% of the total value of fish marketed. Although considered greatest in overall water quality, natural springs contain reduced concentrations of dissolved oxygen and increased concentrations of dissolved gasses. Accordingly, water conditions must be closely monitored to ensure adequate oxygen concentrations and minimize disease, which is especially crucial to trout producers as this is the leading cause of financial loss and accounts for 86% of total losses. The optimal temperatures for achieving the greatest growth rates are between 55 to 65° F and temperatures below 38° F may impair growth.

Typical harvesting occurs when the trout has reached seven to fourteen inches in length and are one half to one pound in weight. This usually occurs between seven to fourteen months of age.

In temperatures outside of the optimal temperature range, reduced nutrient utilization by the digestive system can contribute to nutrient loading of the water and the accompanying reduction in water quality may compromise health of the fish. Feeding rates must be monitored routinely and an ability to adjust feeding rates is important toward optimal trout production. To this end, trout are routinely fed through demand feeders, which consist of hoppers located above the surface of the water that hold the feed pellets and a movable disc that extends into the water by attachment to a pendulum. Trout are trained to feed themselves by operation of the demand feeder, striking of the movable disc releases feed into the water. The advantages of demand feeders in comparison to hand feeding include reduced labor and reduced fluctuations in dissolved oxygen saturation of the water that can occur with inefficient feed utilization associated with overfeeding. Disadvantages may include overfeeding and associated reduction in water quality if the feeders are not properly adjusted.

Tilapia

Worldwide, tilapia production is second in importance only to the production of carp. Increased world production has hindered the domestic production of tilapia as the United States imported four hundred million pounds of tilapia in 2008. The affordable price and mild flavor has contributed to the demand of tilapia and domestic tilapia production is increasing to meet the demand. A 22% increase in domestic tilapia sales occurred between 1998 and 2005. Tilapia contributes 3% of aquaculture's total economic value and 4.7% of the economic value of food fish. As a member of the cichlid family, tilapia are native to Africa and intolerant to low temperatures. Tilapia stop feeding at temperatures below 65° F and the fish are capable of withstanding temperatures of 50 to 52° F for only a few days without pursuant death. Optimal growth occurs at temperatures of 85 to 88° F and at reduced temperature of 72° F, growth is delayed three fold. Such a restriction only allows certain regions of the country to produce the fish outdoors, with California and Florida dominating as the major tilapia producing states. Tilapia production associated with northern climates is often confined indoors. When optimal temperatures are maintained, tilapia are easily managed and can withstand poor water quality with dissolved oxygen concentrations considerably below the tolerance limits for other fish. They are capable of digesting natural food organisms including plankton and decomposing organic matter, which may contribute to 50% of tilapia growth.

The tilapia industry typically conforms to two types of management systems, the mix sex culture and the monosex culture. In the mix sex culture, the males and females are reared together and harvested at the same time, once sexual maturity is reached. In the monosex culture, the males are separated from the females to allow them to attain a greater growth potential. All male culture is desired as male growth rates are two fold greater than females. In the monosex culture, males reach one pound in weight in five to six months

Salmon

Salmon contributes 3.8% of aquaculture's total economic value and 6% of the economic value of food fish. Interestingly, domestic salmon value decreased 60% between 1998 and 2005 and is attributed to increased world production. There are six species of Pacific salmon (Sockeye, Pink, Chum, Coho, Chinook, and Masu) and one species of Atlantic salmon. In the United States, all farmed salmon is Atlantic salmon and over 90% of consumed Atlantic salmon is farmed. In contrast, over 80% of Pacific salmon consumed is wild caught, the remaining farmed species consisting primarily of Chinook and Coho salmon. In Alaska, farming of salmon is banned as it was determined that salmon farming practices were detrimental to wild salmon populations of the region. Washington and Maine are current United States leaders in Atlantic salmon production, with Maine representing an area where Atlantic salmon occurs naturally.

Salmon are anadromous, maturing and spending the majority of their life in the ocean, but returning to fresh water to breed. Successful rearing relies on a two phase system of production: hatching and early growth in fresh water and the transfer of fish to marine net pens for continued growth until harvest. The fresh water phase may last between six months and two years. Milt and roe are harvested from commercially raised adult salmon. Once the eggs are fertilized they are transferred to hatcheries that are designed to mimic the natural spawning nests of salmon. Oxygenated water maintained at 39 to 47° F percolates through the fertilized eggs, supplying oxygen and removing waste. Once hatched, the alevins, which retain a yolk sac, will remain in the incubators. Once the yolk sac is depleted, the alevin will swim to the surface for feeding. At this stage they are referred to as parr and moved to fresh water tanks for feeding. The immature salmon will remain in fresh water tanks until the smolt stage is reached at approximately eighteen months of age, at this time the smolt are transferred to marine net pens that exceed 75 feet in diameter and 50 feet in depth and are anchored to the ocean floor. After twenty-four months in the marine net pens, the salmon are harvested at an average weight of four to ten pounds.

■ **Fig. 14.13** Atlantic salmon. (© Tischenko Irina, 2009. Under license from Shutterstock, Inc.)

Mollusks

Mollusks, including clams, mussels, and oysters contributes 19% of aquacultures total economic value with leading production states including Washington, Virginia, and Louisiana. There are over one hundred species of oyster throughout the world, with only the eastern oyster being of commercial importance. Approximately 60% of total oyster harvest is attributed to cultivated oysters. Oysters spawn between temperatures of 60 to 68° F. Sperm and eggs are released and fertilization occurs within the water. Fertilized eggs develop rapidly and the resulting larvae will feed on algae. As the larvae feed, they become increasingly heavy and can no longer be supported by the water. Consequently, the immature oyster will settle and find a suitable substrate in which to attach and become cemented and grow to maturity.

The most simple of oyster cultivation involves providing a suitable substrate for cementation of larvae where oysters naturally spawn. The substrate may consist of oyster or clam shells. More intensive oyster production involves spawning oysters and hatching larvae within tanks. When ready to set, the larvae are transferred to tanks containing substrate for cementation. Set oysters must be transferred to natural waters for the grow-out phase, which are often estuaries. Oysters reach harvest size between twelve and thirty-six months, the range being dependent on natural water conditions.

Health Management

Many aspects contribute to a healthy environment which allows aquatic species to flourish. No organism is more dependent on their environment than those living in water. Water quality, oxygen content of the water, and pH levels are all crucial factors that attribute to a healthy environment. Correct balances and attentiveness to these factors help to reduce the stress placed on the aquatic organisms in culture. When an animal is stressed, it is significantly more susceptible to disease. Stress can be brought on by rapid changes in water temperature, exposure to low oxygen levels, a fluctuation in pH, poor nutrition, deficient water quality, handling, overstocking, and pollutants. Signs that a fish is stressed include listlessness, decreased feeding, loss of the fish's internal equilibrium and erratic swimming, excessive bottom resting, and rubbing against objects.

A disease is most likely to manifest itself in the immediate days after the stress stimulus has occurred. Decreasing stress greatly correlates to a decrease in disease among the stock. Disease control is especially relevant to the aquaculture industry because of the concentrated nature in which the fish are kept. One disease can be transmitted rapidly from organism to organism. Bacteria, viruses, fungi, and parasites can cause illness in aquatic cultures. A

■ **Fig. 14.14** Oyster beds provide the substrate for the culture of oysters in their traditional aquatic environment. (*Left:* © Christian Musat, 2009. Under license from Shutterstock, Inc. *Right:* © Arwyn, 2009. Under license from Shutterstock, Inc.)

change in fish behavior, lesions, or increased mortality rates are indications of a potential disease problem. The earlier the disease is identified, the greater the likelihood that the disease can be controlled. Chemicals, antibiotics, and vaccines help to control and prevent most outbreaks. Medications can even be distributed through the feed. However, all drugs administered to the fish are closely regulated by the United States Department of Agriculture and must be in compliance with their standards.

Proper sanitation practices can greatly reduce the risk of a disease epidemic. Supplies that are used in one tank should not be used in another unless sanitized between usages. People also can introduce diseases and some facilities may require special clothing to be worn. Iodine foot baths are common to disinfect the bottoms of shoes before entering a culture chamber room. The strictest facilities are regimented around a color system of sanitized, coverall clothing. In an effort to avoid cross contamination, no person is allowed to enter a room unless wearing the corresponding color.

■ **Fig. 14.15** Members of the cichlid family protect the offspring through mouth brooding. Many of the tilapia species are maternal mouth brooders, in which the female gathers and incubates the eggs in her mouth either before or after fertilization. During mouth brooding the female will seldom eat and weight loss during the incubation period is common. Tilapia species commonly used as food fish extend mouth brooding to the fry stage and must be forced to release the developing fry for production rearing. (© Mitch Aunger, 2009. Under license from Shutterstock, Inc.)

Capacity of Production

Unlike agriculture livestock, the reproduction in aquatic animals varies by species. All species produce sexually. Most aquatic species comply with a male/female classification. Some however, are hermaphrodites and possess both male and female sex organs. If a fish has both functioning gonads at the same time, it is known as a *synchronous hermaphrodite*. If one gonad functions at the beginning of life and then alternates to the other, opposite gonad, the fish is known as a *sequential hermaphrodite*. In addition, the sex of all aquatic species is not determined at birth and can be influenced by environmental factors, including temperature, in the early life stages.

The actual reproduction process also varies greatly in aquatic species. Most fish lay thousands of eggs, less than a millimeter in diameter. For example, the adult catfish lays approximately three thousand eggs per pound of body weight or eighteen thousand eggs for a mature female. Many fish deposit their eggs into the water current and do not provide parental care to the fertilized eggs or resulting larvae. Although, some fish are known to prepare a spawning site and guard the fertilized eggs until hatch. For example, female tilapia brood the eggs in their mouth after fertilization and male catfish build the nest and guard the fertilized eggs, protecting the eggs even from the spawning female. In addition, fish may spawn multiple times per year, once per year, or in the case of the Pacific salmon, once in their lifetime.

Challenges to the Industry

Expansion

There is certainly room for expansion within the United States aquaculture industry as the country currently imports 45% of all seafood consumed. However, expansion poses challenges to the industry, especially in marine segments. Many environmental groups are closely guarding native waters and are fearful of ecological changes that might ensue if the marine aquaculture industry expands. These concerns include worry over increased diseases that could devastate natural fish populations, genetic alteration to existing natural species as farmed species escape commercial enclosures and interbreed, pollution from concentrated rearing systems, and decreasing aesthetics. Commercial fishermen are wary of expansion as some perceive aquaculture as competition. Concerns of the effects of aquaculture sites on the navigation of the seaways also have been voiced.

Environment

The available clean water in North America is declining. Some aquaculture systems rely on the use of clean water and the monetary and socioeconomic cost of water is increasing.

Freshwater aquaculture faces challenges as most of the fresh water resources within the United States are already employed for agriculture, industry, or civic needs. However, there is an innovative and potential solution for this obstruction, known as the Joint Aquaculture/Agriculture Water Sharing, or JAWS. This concept involves merging aquaculture endeavors with the water intended for agriculture irrigation. In this system, the aquaculture facility would have first use of the water, but instead of cleaning and returning it to the water supply, the water would be directly transferred to an agriculture

partner. This saves the aquaculture producer from spending money to clean the water, while also benefiting the agriculture producer by supplying the farm with water containing nutrients, thus saving the agriculture producer some fertilizing costs. Both partners would split the initial costs of water. Experts suggest that this process could double the aquaculture industry in the United States if only 4% of the water used in Western irrigation would be used in this manner.

Predation

Predation of aquaculture species by birds, mammals, and invertebrates is estimated to contribute to millions of dollars in economic loss annually. Of these predators, birds including herons, grackles (black birds), mallards, kingfishers, and ospreys are most often encountered in United States aquaculture facilities. Besides the obvious loss caused by actual consumption of fish stock, the predators also bring about loss by increasing stress and injury, and reducing appetite and feeding behaviors. In addition, the predators may carry diseases and transmit these to the fish cultures. Changes in aquaculture

■ **Fig. 14.16**　Netting is used over marine net pens to deter predation, which contributes to major economic losses annually in the culture of aquatic organisms. (© Lee Torrens, 2009. Under license from Shutterstock, Inc.)

■ **Fig. 14.17**   Consumption of fish has remained static at sixteen pounds per person annually in recent years despite the recognition of the health benefits afforded by adding fish to the diet. (© Dusan Zidar, 2009. Under license from Shutterstock, Inc.)

practices that include deepening ponds and raceways and maintaining steep banks, delaying transition of fingerlings from indoor to outdoor rearing facilities, reducing stocking density, and discouraging fish to surface by changing feeding practices have been encouraged to reduce the losses associated with predation.

Fish as a Food Commodity

Like other animal meats, fish is a nutritious food that contains many vitamins, minerals, and high value protein. However, fish contains fewer calories, less fat, and less cholesterol than do other meats. It is a general concept that seafood is a healthy choice and can be a beneficial addition to a balanced diet. The exact nutritional makeup of fish varies by the species consumed; however, many fish contain little, if any, saturated fats. Some fish species have a high oil content that can be beneficial to the consumer. Contained within this oil are omega three fatty acids which can help to reduce blood cholesterol and improve heart health. Some fish are also a plentiful source of natural iodine and fluorine in addition to magnesium, phosphorus, iron, and copper. Because of these components, in addition to its high quality protein and its low levels of fat and cholesterol, some nutritionists suggest replacing a portion of traditional meats with fish.

Emerging Issues: Animal Welfare

"The greatness of a nation and its moral progress can be judged by the way its animals are treated."
— *Mahatma Ghandi (1869–1948)*

Animal Welfare: A Historical Perspective

There is no universally accepted definition for animal welfare. In general, animal welfare represents the view that animals under human care should be maintained under conditions that do not pose unnecessary harm. Concern over animal welfare dates to 2000 B.C. and the Indus Valley Civilization. There was a religious belief that ancestors return to earth in animal form, and therefore animals must be treated with respect by humans. Throughout the world, many cultures have developed codes, laws, and regulations that protect animals. In 1876, the Cruelty to Animals Act was established and created a central governing body that reviewed and approved all animal use in research. In 1966, the United States Animal Welfare Act was enacted and was the first federal law protecting the welfare of laboratory animals. Subsequent amendments to the Act have expanded coverage to animals in commerce, exhibition, teaching, and testing. In part, the Animal Welfare Act was initiated following public outcry after the release of stories of dogs used in biomedical research originating from theft, and the unsuitable living conditions of dog facilities that supplied animals for research. The initial passing of the Animal Welfare Act set minimum standards for the handling, sale, and transport of cats, dogs, rabbits, nonhuman primates, guinea pigs, and hamsters. The amendment of 1976 ensured proper handling during transportation and established standards for feed, water, and temperature during transport. In 2002, the definition of animal recognized by the Act was expanded to include mice, rats, and birds. In 2007, the buying, selling, or transportation of instruments used in animal fighting was prohibited through the Animal Welfare Act.

■ **Fig. 15.1** Concern over the living conditions of animals housed for research prompted the enactment of the Animal Welfare Act in 1966. (© Jose AS Reyes, 2009. Under license from Shutterstock, Inc.)

Ethics

Ethics are a system of moral values that provide the basis for the determination of what a person believes is right or wrong. Thereby, this system provides a set of principles that outline acceptable conduct and ultimately underlies an individual's decision to do what is acceptable with respect to animal welfare. An ongoing moral dilemma that has been under consideration for hundreds of years is whether humans should raise and kill animals for food; and if so, how they should be raised and killed. While many people, especially those of agrarian societies see the raising and harvesting of animals for meat as a perfectly acceptable practice; it is still important to consider the moral and ethical implications of raising and killing animals for human consumption.

Ethics are intertwined with animal welfare and animal rights. As rational beings, with the ability to reason and form a system of moral beliefs, the question arises: Do humans have the right to use other organisms for their own benefit?

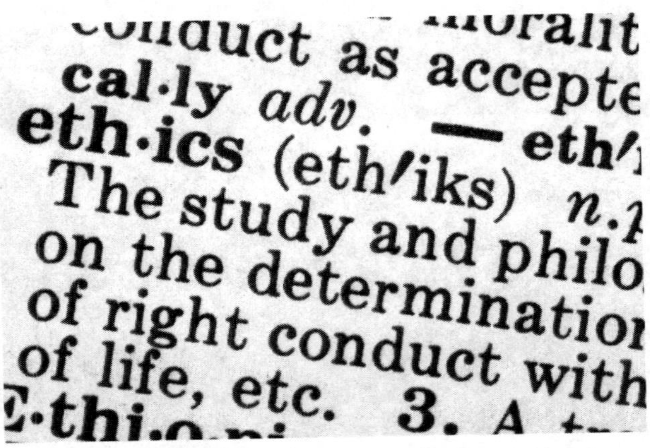

Animal Welfare versus Animal Rights

Animal welfare is the viewpoint that animals should not suffer unnecessarily and, under human care, should be provided with an adequate environment and adequate provisions to meet their physiological and behavioral needs. Those that support animal welfare believe that it is acceptable to use animals for food, research, recreation, and to keep as companions assuming that the animals are maintained humanely. As defined by the American Veterinary Medical Association (AVMA), animal welfare is, "A humane responsibility that encompasses all aspects of animal well-being, including proper housing, management, nutrition, disease prevention and treatment, responsible care, humane handling, and when necessary humane euthanasia." On the other hand, animal rights is the belief that animals have intrinsic rights to life and liberty, just as humans. Animal rights theorists state that nonhuman animals should be allowed to live according to their own nature, free from harm, abuse, and exploitation by man. Support for animals rights leads to the exclusion of animals for farming, research, and entertainment. As there is no uniformly accepted definition of animal welfare,

■ **Fig. 15.2** Ethics, an individual's values of right and wrong, underpin the decisions to accept or reject the practices of animal use. (© robyn Mackenzie, 2009. Under license from Shutterstock, Inc.)

there is no universally accepted definition of animal rights. Amongst supporters of animal rights, the defining line that distinguishes between which animals deserve these rights and which animals do not is debated. Within the animal rights movement advocates may be categorized, either as reformists or abolitionists. Animal rights abolitionists are more extreme in their viewpoints and advocate the total abandonment of any animal use. Reformists are generally less extreme in their viewpoints and are usually willing to work within the system to change the methods of animal use.

Approaches to Animal Welfare

In order to understand and be informed of the impact of animal care practices on the physiological and behavioral needs of animals, there must be a framework to assess, study, and define animal welfare. Currently, there are five primary approaches to the study of animal welfare: feelings based, animal-choices, nature of the species, the five freedoms, and biological-functioning based.

Feelings

Feelings based approach defines animal welfare in terms of emotions. Most agree that animals are capable of basic emotions: anger, fear, joy and happiness. Feelings evolved as a means of protecting the basic needs of animals and are suggested to play a role in survival. For example, fear evolved as a flexible means of avoiding danger. The feelings based approach emphasizes a reduction in negative emotions such as pain and fear and an increase in positive emotions such as comfort and pleasure. Although the mental well-being of an animal is considered an essential component of animal welfare, the problem arises with defining emotions. Feelings are subjective and only available to the animal experiencing the emotion. As there is no common language between humans and other animals, animals can not relate their emotions and only by analogy can humans assume the emotions experienced by animals. Emotions are often tied to a bodily response; however, most animals react physiologically in the same manner to positive and negative experiences. Heart rate may increase in response to the presence of a mate or the presence of a predator.

■ **Fig. 15.3**   Allowing an animals to make its own choice may not be in the animals best interest. (© Sue Smith, 2009. Under license from Shutterstock, Inc.)

Animal Choices

In the animal-choices approach, the animal is allowed to choose between certain aspects of its environment and the assumption is made that the animal will choose according to what is in its best interests. Choices made by an animal, however, may be influenced by prior experiences and not represent the best interest of the animal. Furthermore, animal choices are difficult to interpret and the choices made may have adverse outcomes. For the wild animal, many choices are based on survival. Without natural selection, how are preferences driven and does this reflect welfare? For example, feast or famine is a survival mechanism of the lion. When prey is secured, the lion feasts and will gorge as food is plentiful and the certainty of the next meal is not guaranteed. Gluttony is important to allow the animal to survive periods of famine until the next meal is secured. For the domesticated cat, the instinct to feast may still reside. If the cat is fed *ad-libitum* it may feast; however, without the period of famine to follow, the animal will put on excess weight and obesity may occur. The animal's choice, therefore, is not in its best welfare interests.

Nature of the Species

The nature of the species approach requires the animal to be raised in an environment that allows it to express its complete range of behaviors. In general, this approach states that animals should be raised in their natural environment in natural ways. The

term natural is not clearly defined, but is often equated with the wild environment and behaviors displayed by non-domesticated animals. Although a common approach early in the study of animal welfare, it does not consider the modification of behaviors as a consequence of domestication and some behaviors that occur in the wild could be detrimental. For example, pre-weaning pig mortality exceeds 20% in wild pig populations; however, mortality rates are less than 10% in indoor farrowed pigs. Is it acceptable to permit increased mortality simply because the animals are considered free to express what is interpreted as normal behaviors?

Five Freedoms

The five freedoms approach to animal welfare outlines the elements necessary for ideal welfare and defines the husbandry and resources required to promote this ideal welfare state. The five freedoms and provisions are as follows:

1. Freedom from thirst, hunger, and malnutrition by ready access to fresh water and a diet to maintain full health and vigor.
2. Freedom from discomfort by providing a suitable environment including shelter and a comfortable resting area.
3. Freedom from pain, injury, and disease by prevention or rapid diagnosis and treatment.
4. Freedom from fear and distress by ensuring conditions that avoid mental suffering.

5. Freedom to express normal behavior by providing sufficient space, proper facilities, and company of the animal's own kind.

The five freedoms approach has been adopted widely and has had a significant impact on the minimum standards required for animal welfare. This approach, however, does not consider social behaviors and there is not a universally accepted definition of what constitutes normal behaviors.

Biological Functioning

Another approach to animal welfare is the biological-functioning based approach. Because of difficulties associated with some of the aforementioned practices in defining welfare, many scientists prefer a more traditional measure based on body function.

■ **Fig. 15.4** Defining what constitutes normal behavior is a primary limitation to the five freedoms approach to animal welfare. (© Jana Shea, 2009. Under license from Shutterstock, Inc.)

Animals will adapt to a new environment or situation and a failure to adapt will lead to a loss in biological functioning. This approach aims to define the biological costs associated with the environment. For example, does the environment result in decreased growth, reproductive failure, injury, disease, or death? It has been suggested under this approach that welfare reflects the status of the animal considering it attempts to contend with its environment. Welfare is then appraised by how much has to be done to cope (the biological responses elicited) and is coping successful (measured by a lack of biological costs, ie deterioration of growth). Although a preferred method of welfare assessment by scientists, it only considers the physical and not the emotional needs of the animals.

Animal Welfare Issues

As the stance to the use of animals differs, approaches to animal welfare differ, emphasizing different aspects of an animal's well being. With the advent of industrialized farming techniques, the growth in the number of companion animals, and the use of animals for research; animal welfare will remain a major social and political issue. The key to improving animal welfare resides in the attitudes and behaviors of humans, since humans have dominion. Although science attempts to express animal welfare as a scientific concept, quality of life is difficult to measure. Between the demands of an ever increasing population and the welfare of the sentient species entrusted in human care, striking the correct balance may never be universally attained.

Reading List

Adams, G.P., M.H. Ratto, W. Huanca, and J. Singh. 2005. Ovulation-inducing factor in the seminal plasma of alpacas and llamas. Biol. Reprod. 73:452-457.

Alaska Department of Fish and Game. Gaudet, D. 2002. Atlantic salmon: a white paper.

Albarella, U., K. Dobney, A. Ervynck, and P. Rowley-Conway. 2008. Pigs and humans: 10,000 years of interaction. Oxford; Oxford University Press.

Alberts, B., D. Bray, J. Lewis, M. Raff, K. Roberts, J.D. Watson. 1994. Molecular biology of the cell. 3rd ed. New York: Garland Publishing.

Alpaca registry statistics. From Alpaca Registry, Inc. 2009. Retrieved from http://www.alpacaregistry.com/.

American Horse Council. 2005. The economic impact of the horse industry on the United States. Washington, D.C.: Deloitte Consulting, LLP.

American Veterinary Medical Association. American College of Animal Welfare Organizing Committee. Animal Welfare. Retrieved from http://www.avma.org/issues/animal_welfare/default.asp.

Andersen, I.L., S. Berg, and K.E. Boe. 2005. Crushing of piglets by the mother sow (*Sus scrofa*)-purely accidental or a poor mother? Appl. Anim. Behav. Sci. 93:229-243.

Bahr, J. 2008. The Chicken as a Model Organism. From the Sourcebook of Models for Biomedical Research. Totowa: Humana Press Inc.

Baldwin, J.M. 1896. Heredity and instinct (I). Science.

Barnett, J.L., P.H. Hemsworth, G.M. Cronin, E.C. Jongman, and G.D. Hutson. 2001. A review of the welfare issues for sows and piglets in relation to housing. Aust. J. Agric. Res. 52:1-28.

Baumans, V. 2004. Use of animals in experimental research: an ethical dilemma? Gene Therapy. 11:S64-S66.

Bauman, D.E., I.H. Mather, R.J. Wall, and A.L. Lock. 2006. Major advances associated with the biosynthesis of milk. J. Dairy Sci. 89:1235-1243.

Bearden, H.J., J.W. Fuquay, and S.T. Willard. 2004. Applied animal reproduction. 6th ed. Upper Saddle River: Pearson Prentice Hall.

Beaumont, W. 1833. Experiments and observations on the gastric juice and the physiology of digestion. Pittsburgh: Allen.

Behringer, R.B. G.S. Eaking, and M.B. Renfree. 2006. Mammalian diversity: gametes, embryos, and reproduction. Reprod. Fertil. Dev. 18:99-107.

Bell, F.R. 1972. Sleep in the larger domesticated animals. Proc. Roy. Soc. Med. 65:176-177.

Belloc, H. 1957. Stories, essays, and poems. San Diego, CA: Dent.

Board on Agriculture and Natural Resources. 2008. Changes in the sheep industry in the United States. Making the transition from tradition. Washington, D.C: The National Academies Press.

Bradford, G.E. 1999. Contributions of animal agriculture to meeting global food demand. Livest. Prod. Sci. 59:95-112.

Brady, C. 2008. An illustrated guide to animal science terminology. Clifton Park: Thomson Delmar Learning.

Brillat-Savarin, J-A. 1985. The philosopher in the kitchen. Middlesex: Penguin Books.

Broom, D.M. 1986. Indicators of poor welfare. Br. Vet. J. 142:524-526.

Broom, D.M. 1988. The scientific assessment of animal welfare. Appl. Anim. Behav. Sci. 20:5-19.

Broom, D.M. 1991. Animal welfare: concepts and measurement. J. Anim. Sci. 69;4167-4175.

Bruford, M., D. Bradley, G. Luikart. 2003. DNA markers reveal the complexity of livestock domestication. Nature. 4:900-910.

Cain, K. and D. Garling. 1993. Trout culture in the north central region. North Central Regional Aquaculture Center. Fact Sheet 108.

Campbell, K.L. and J.R. Campbell. 2009. Companion animals: their biology, care, health, and management. 2nd ed. Upper Saddle River: Pearson Prentice Hall.

Campbell, J.R. and J.F. Lasley. 1969. The science of animals that serve mankind. New York: McGraw-Hill.

Capuco, A.V. and R.M. Akers. 2009. The origin and evolution of lactation. J. Biol. 8:37-40.

Carpenter, K.J. 2003. A short history of nutritional science: Part 1 (1785-1885). J. Nutr. 133:638-645.

Carpenter, K.J. 2003. A short history of nutritional science: Part 2 (1885-1912). J. Nutr. 133:975-984.

Carpenter, K.J. 2003. A short history of nutritional science: Part 3 (1912-1944). J. Nutr. 133:3023-3032.

Carpenter, K.J. 2003. A short history of nutritional science: Part 4 (1945-1985). J. Nutr. 133:3331-3342.

Cheeke, P.R. 2004. Contemporary issues in animal agriculture. 3rd ed. Upper Saddle River: Pearson Prentice Hall.

Chessa, B. et. al. 2009. Revealing the history of sheep domestication using retrovirus integrations. Science. 324:532-536.

Clarke, A.S. 1996. Maternal gestational stress alters adaptive and social behavior in adolescent rhesus monkey offspring. Infant Behav. Dev. 19:451-461.

Clauss, M., A. Schwarm, S. Ortmann, D. Alber, E.J. Flach, R. Kühne, J. Hummel, W.J. Streich, and H. Hofer. 2004. Intake, ingesta retention, particle size distribtution and digestibility in the hippopotamidae. Comp. Biochem. Physiol. A. 139:449-459.

Combs, G.F. Jr. 1998. The Vitamins: Fundamental Aspects in Nutrition and Health. 2nd ed. San Diego: Academic Press.

Correa, J.E. 2008. Nutritive value of goat meat. Alabama Cooperative Extension System. UNP-0061.

Costa, D.A. and D.J. Reinemann. 2004. The purpose of the milking routine and comparative physiology of milk removal. Paper presented at the National Mastitis Council Meeting.

Crawford, R.D. 1990. Origin and history of poultry species. In R.D. Crawford (Ed.) Poultry breeding and genetics. Amsterdam: Elsevier.

Cunningham, M., M.A. Latour, and D. Acker. 2005. Animal Science and Industry. 7th ed. Upper Saddle River: Pearson Education, Inc.

Damron, W.S. 2006. Introduction to Animal Science: Global, Biological, Social, and Industry Perspectives. 3rd ed. Upper Saddle River: Pearson Education Inc.

Darwin, C. 1872. The expression of the emotions in man and animals. London: John Murray.

Dehoux, J-P. and P. Gianello. 2007. The importance of large animal models in transplantation. Frontiers in Bioscience. 12:4864-4880.

Dekkers, J.C.M. 2004. Commercial application of marker- and gene-selected selection in livestock: strategies and lessons. J. Anim. Sci. 82:E313-E328.

DeVries, A., M. Overton, J. Fetrow, K. Leslie, S. Eicker, and G. Rogers. 2007. Exploring the impact of sexed semen on the structure of the dairy industry. J. Dairy Sci. 91:847-856.

Drake, A., D. Fraser, D.M. Weary. 2008. Parent-offspring resource allocation in domestic pigs. Behav. Eco. Sociobiol. 62:309-319.

Dryden, G. McL. 2008. Animal Nutrition Science. Wallingford:CABI Publishing.

Duncan, I.J.H. 2005. Science-based assessment of animal welfare: farm animals. Rev. Sci. Tech. Off. Int. Epiz. 24:483-492.

Engle, C., G. Greaser, and J. Harper. 2000. Agriculture alternatives: Meat goat production. Pennsylvania State University Extension. ps37409.

Ensminger, M.E. and R.C. Perry. 1997. Beef cattle science. 7th ed. Danville: Interstate Publishers Inc.

Evans, J.P., A. Borton, H.F. Hintz, and L.D. van Vleck (Ed.). 1990. The Horse. 2nd ed. New York: W.H. Freeman and Co.

Evans, P. 2005. Equine vision and its effects on behavior. Utah State University Cooperative Extension Service. AG/Equine/2005-03.

Evershed, R.P., S. Payne, A.G. Sherratt, M.S. Copley, J. Coolidge, D. Urem-Kotsu, et. al. 2008. Earliest date for milk use in the Near East and southeastern Europe linked to cattle herding. Nature. 455:528-531.

Field, T.G. and R.E. Taylor. 2008. Scientific farm animal production: an introduction to animal science. 9th ed. Upper Saddle River: Pearson Prentice Hall.

Food and Agriculture Organization of the United Nations, Fisheries and Aquaculture Department. Cultured Aquatic Species Fact Sheets. Retrieved from http://www.fao.org/fishery/culturedspecies/search/en.

Food and Agriculture Organization of the United Nations, FAO Fisheries Department. 2006. State of the world aquaculture. Tech.500.

Food and Agriculture Organization of the United Nations, International Committee on Animal recording. Cardellino, R., A. Rosati, and C. Mosconi. 2004. Current status of genetic resources, recordings, and production systems in African, Asian, and American camelids. TS.no.2.

Food and Agriculture Organization of the United Nations, United Nations Development Program, Regional Small Scale -Coastal Fisheries Development Project. Rabanal, H. 1988. History of Aquaculture. ASEAN/SF/88/Tech.7.

Foote, R.H. 1987. In vitro fertilization and embryo transfer in domestic animals: Applications in animals and implications for humans. J. Assisted Repro. and Genetics. 4:73-88.

Foote, R.H. 2002. The history of artificial insemination: selected notes and notables. J. Anim. Sci. 80:1-10.

Frandson, R.D., W.L. Wilke, and A.D. Fails. 2003. Anatomy and physiology of farm animals. 6th ed. Baltimore: Lippincott Williams and Wilkins.

Fricker, J. 2001. The pig: a new model of atherosclerosis. DDT. 6;921-922.

Fumihito, A., T. Miyake, S. Sumi, M. Takada, S. Ohno, and K. Kondo. 1994. One subspecies of the red junglefowl *(Gallus gallus gallus)* suffices as the matriarchic ancestor of all domestic breeds. PNAS. 91:12505-12509.

Gatlin L.A., M. T. See, D.K. Larick, X. Lin, and L. Odle. 2002. Conjugated linoleic acid in combination with supplemental dietary fat alters pork fat quality. J. Nutr. 132:3105-3112.

Gillespie, J.R. 1998. Animal Science. Albany: Delmar Publishers.

Grant, R. 2007. Taking Advantage of Natural Behavior Improves Dairy Cow Performance. Presented at: Western Dairy Management Conference Reno, NV. March 7-9. Retrieved from http://www.extension.org/pages/Taking_Advantage_of_Natural_Behavior_Improves_Dairy_Cow_Performance.

Griffiths, J.T. 2008. Equine Science: basic knowledge for horse people of all ages. Gaithersburg: Equine Network Publishers.

Grützner, B., Nixon, and R.C. Jones. 2008. Reproductive biology in egg-laying mammals. Sex. Dev. 2:115-127.

Hendricks, B. 1996. International encyclopedia of the horse. Norman: University of Oklahoma Press.

Hewson, C. 2003. What is animal welfare? Common definitions and their practical consequences. Can. Vet. J. 44:496-499.

Hinshaw, J. 1990. Trout production: feeds and feeding methods. Southern Regional Aquaculture Center. SRAC223.

Hodges, J. 1999. Animals and value in society. Livest. Prod. Sci. 58:159-194.

Hogan, J.S. and K.L. Smith. 1987. A Practical Look at Environmental Mastitis. Compendium on Continuing Education for the Practicing Veterinarian. 9: F342.

Holden, P.J. and M.E. Ensminger. 2006. Swine science. 7th ed. Upper Saddle River: Pearson Prentice Hall.

Hooke, R. 1667. Micrographia: or some physiological descriptions of minute bodies made by magnifying glasses: with observations and inquiries thereupon. London: John Martyn.

Horton, H.R., L.A. Moran, K.G. Scrimgeour, M.D. Perry, and J.D. Rawn. 2006. Principles of Biochemistry. 4th ed. Upper Saddle River: Pearson Education Inc.

Hovey, R.C., J.F. Trott, and B.K. Vonderhaar. 2002. Establishing a framework for the functional mammary gland: from endocrinology to morphology. J. Mammary Gland Biol. 7:17-38.

Jansen, T., P. Forster, M.A. Levine, H. Oelke, M. Hurles, C. Renfrew, J. Weber, and K. Olek. 2002. Mitochondrial DNA and the origins of the domestic horse. PNAS. 99:10905-10910.

Jiang, Z. and M.F. Rothschild. 2007. Swine genomics comes of age. Int. J. Biol. Sci. 3:129-131.

Johannsen, W. 1909. Elemente der exakten Erblichkeitslehre. Gustav Fischer, Jena.

Johnson, D.E. 2007. Contributions of animal nutrition research to nutritional principles: energetic. J. Nutr. 137:698-701.

Johnson, L.W. 1994. Llama nutrition. Veterinary Clinics of North America: Food Animal Practice. 10:187-201.

Josephson, M. 2005. Stendhal or the pursuit of happiness. New York: Jorge Pinto Books.

Jurgens, M.H. 1993. Animal Feeding and Nutrition., 7th ed. Dubuque: Kendall Hunt Publishing Company.

Kadwell, M., M. Fernandez H.F. Stanley, R. Baldi, J.C. Wheeler, R. Rosadio, and M.W. Bruford. 2001. Genetic analysis reveals the wild ancestors of the llama and the alpaca. Proc. R. Soc. Land. B. 268:2575-2584.

Kaushik, S.J. 1999. Animals for work, recreation, and sports. Livest. Prod. Sci. 59:145-154.

Keeling, L.J. and H.W. Gonyou. 2001. Social behavior in farm animals. Wallingford:CABI Publishing.

Kessel, A.L. and L. Brent. 1998. Cage toys reduce abnormal behavior in individually housed pigtail macques. J. Applied Anim. Welfare Sci. 1:227-234.

Kjaer, J.B., P. Sorensen, G. Su. 2001. Divergent selection on feather pecking behavior in laying hens (*Gallus gallus domesticus*). App. Anim. Behaviour Sci. 71:229-239.

Kues, W.A. and H. Niemann. 2004. The contribution of farm animals to human health. Trends in Biotech. 22:286-294.

Kunz, T.H. and D.J. Hosken. 2008. Male lactation: why, why not and is it care? Trends Ecol. Evol. 24:81-85.

Lacy, M. and M. Czarick. 1998. Mechanical harvesting of broilers. Poultry Sci. 77:1794-1797.

Lai L., J.X. Kang, R. Li, L. Wang, W.T. Witt, H.Y. Yong, et. al. 2006. Generation of cloned transgenic pigs rich in omega-3 fatty acids. Nat. Biotechnol. 24:435-6.

Lacy, R.C. 1997. Importance of genetic variation to the viability of animal population. J. Mammal. 320-335.

Lavoisier, A.L. and P.S. Laplace. 1780. Mémoire sur la chaleur. Mém. Acad. Sci. Paris. 355-408.

Lecce, J. 1979. Intestinal barriers to water-soluble macromolecules. Environ. Health Perspec. 33:57-60.

Lechner-Doll, M., W. von Engelhardt, A.M. Abbas, H.M. Mousa, L. Luciano, and E. Reale. 1995. Particularities in forestomach anatomy, physiology and biochemistry of camelids compared to ruminants. In Tisserand J.-L. (ed.). *Elevage et alimentation du dromadaire = Camel production and nutrition* (19-32). Zaragoza:CIHEAM-IAMZ.

Lewandowski, R. 2003. Goat: The other red meat. Buckeye Meat Goat Newsletter, The Ohio State University Extension. 1:7-8.

Lindsay, S.R. and G.E. Burrows. 2000. Handbook of applied dog behavior and training, volume 1: adaptation and learning. Ames: Iowa State Press.

Leeuwenhoek, A. 1678. Des natis é semine genital animalculis. R. Soc. (Lond.) Philos. Trans. 12:1040-1043.

Logothetis, N.K. 2004. Francis Crick 1916-2004. Nature Neuroscience. 7:1027-1028.

Ludwi, A., M. Pruvost, M. Reissmann, N. Benecke, G.A. Brockmann, P. Castaños, M. Cieslak, S. Lippold, L. Llorente, A-S. Malaspinas, M. Slatkin, and M. Hofreiter. 2009. Coat color variation at the beginning of horse domestication. Science. 324:485.

Luginbuhl, J-M. 1998. Breeds and production traits of meat goats. North Carolina Cooperative Extension Service. ANS00-603MG.

Luginbuhl, J-M, J.T. Green, J.P. Mueller, and M.H. Poore. 1996. Meat goats in land and forage management. Southeast Regional Meat Goat Production Symposium. Florida A&M University, Tallahassee.

Lunney, J.K. 2007. Advances in swine biomedical model genomics. Int. J. Biol. Sci. 3:179-184.

MacHugh, D.E. and D.G. Bradley. 2001. Livestock genetic origins: goats buck the trend. PNAS. 98:5382-5384.

Marchant-Forde, J.N. 2009. The welfare of pigs. Netherlands: Springer.

Masataka, N., H. Koda, N. Urasopon, and K. Watanbe. 2009. Free-ranging macaque mothers exaggerate tool-using behavior when observed by offspring. PloS One. 4:e4768.

Matilla-Sandholm, T. and M. Saarela (Ed.) 2003. Functional Foods. Cambridge: Woodhead Publishing Limited.

Maynard, L.A. 1951. Animal Nutrition. New York: McGraw-Hill Inc.

McNeilly, A.S. 2001. Lactational control of reproduction. Reprod. Fertile. Dev. 13:583-590.

McPherron, A.C. and S-J. Lee. 1997. Double muscling in cattle due to mutations in the myostatin gene. Proc. Natl. Acad. Sci. 94:12457-12461.

Mepham, T.B. (Ed.) 1983. Biochemistry of lactation. Amesterdam: Elsevier.

Meyers, R.A. and B. Worm. 2003. Rapid worldwide depletion of predatory fish communities. Nature. 423:280-283.

Min, B.R., S.P. Hart, T. Sahlu, and L.D. Satter. 2005. The effect of diets on milk production and composition, and on lactation curves in pastured dairy goats. J. Dairy Sci. 88:2604-2615.

Morin, D.E., L.L. Rowan, W.L. Hurley, and W.E. Braselton. 2005. Composition of milk from llamas in the United States. J. Dairy Sci. 78:1713-1720.

Mosher, D., P. Quignon, C.D. Bistamante, N.B. Sutter, C.S. Mellersh, H.G. Parker, and E.A. Ostrander. 2007. A mutation in the myostatin gene increases muscle mass and enhances racing performance in heterzygote dogs. PLoS Genetics. 3:e79.

Mozdziak, P.E. and J.N. Petitte. 2004. Status of transgenic chicken models for developmental biology. Dev. Dynamics. 229:414-421.

Nash, C.E. (Ed.). 2001. The net-pen salmon farming industry in the Pacific Northwest. U.S. Dept. Commer., NOAA Tech. Memo. NMFS-NWFSC-49, 125.

National Sustainable Agriculture Information Service. Appropriate Technology Transfer in Rural Areas. Beetz, A. Grass-based and seasonal dairying. 1998: ATTRA Publication #CT079. Retrieved from http://attra.ncat.org/attra-pub/gbdairy.html.

Orwell, G. 1996. Animal Farm: a fairy story, 50th Anniversary ed. New York: Penguin Books Ltd.

Osborne, L. 2002. Got silk? The New Work Times. 6:49.

Pavlov, I. 1967. In Nobel Lectures, Physiology or Medicine 1901-1921. Amsterdam: Elsevier Publishing Company.

Parker, R. 2007. Equine Science. 3rd ed. Clifton Park: Thompson Delmar Learning.

Pauly, D., V. Christensen, S. Guénette, T. Pitcher, U.R. Samaila, C. Walters, R. Watson, and D. Zeller. 2002. Towards sustainability in world fisheries. Nature. 418:689-695.

Peaker, A. 2002. The mammary gland in mammalian evolution: a brief commentary on some of the consepts. J. Mammary Gland Biol. 7:347-353.

Pennington, J. and M.McCarter. 2007. Marketing of meat goats. University of Arkansas Cooperative Extension Services. FSA3094.

Perkins, B.E. 1995. Aquacultured oyster products: inspection, quality, handling, storage, safety. Southern Regional Aquaculture Center. SRAC434.

Perry, T.W., A.E. Cullison, and R.S. Lowrey. 2003. Feeds and Feeding, 6th ed. Upper Saddle River: Pearson Education, Inc.

Pigs domesticated 'many times'. 2005. BBC News. Retrieved from http://news.bbc.co.uk/2/hi/science/nature/4337435.stm.

Pigs: Webster's quotations, facts, and phrases. 2008. San Diego: Icon Group International Inc.

Polidori, P., C. Renieri, M. Antonini, P. Passamonti, and F. Pucciarelli. 2007. Meat fatty acid composition of llama (*Lama glama*) reared in the Andean highlands. 75:356-358.

Pond, C.M. 1977. The significance of lactation in the evolution of mammals. Evolution. 31:177-199.

Pond, W.G., D.C. Church, K.R. Pond, and P.A. Schoknecht. 2005. Basic Animal Nutrition and Feeding. 5th ed. Hoboken: John Wiley and Sons, Inc.

Porteus, J. 2002. Slick birds are wearing wool. Knitted pullovers protect penguins from oil discharge. Nature News. Retrieved from http://www.nature.com/news/2002/020122/full/news020121-3.html.

Price, E.O. 1984. Behavioural aspects of animal domestication. Rev. Biol. 59:1–32.

Price, E.O. 1999. Behavioral development in animals undergoing domestication. Appl. Anim. Behav. Sci. 65:245-271.

Prout, W. 1824. On the nature of the acid and saline matters usually existing in the stomach of animals. Philos. Trans. R. Soc. Lond. 114:45-49.

Purser, J. and N. Forteath. 2003. Salmonids. In J.S. Lucas & P.C. Southgate (Eds.), Aquaculture: Farming Aquatic Animals and Plants. Oxford: Blackwell Publishing, 295-320.

Regional multi-state interpretation of small farm financial data from the third year report on 2002 great lakes grazng network grazing dairy data. 2004. Great Lakes Grazing Network. Fact Sheet 5: Grazing versus Confinement Farms-Year 3.

Reimer, J.J. 2006. Vertical integration in the pork industry. Amer. J. Agr. Econ. 88:234-248.

Reiner, R. and F. Bryant. 1983. A different sort of sheep. Rangelands. 5:106-108.

Robinson, R. 2008. For mammals, loss of yolk and gain of milk went hand in hand. PLoS Biology. 6:e77.

Rooney, M.B. and J. Sleeman. 1998. Effects of selected behavioral enrichment devices on behavior of western lowland gorillas. J. Applied Anim. Welfare Sci. 1:339-351.

Scanes, C.G. 2003. Biology of growth of domestic animals. Ames: Iowa State Press.

Scanes, C.G., G. Brant, and M.E. Ensminger. 2004. Poultry Science. 4th ed. Upper Saddle River: Prentice Education, Inc.

Schilo, K.K. 2009. Reproductive physiology of mammals: from farm to field and beyond. Clifton Park: Delmar Cengage Learning.

Schook, L., C. Beattie, J. Beaver, S. Donovan, R. Jamison, F. Zuckerman, et. al. 2005. Swine in biomedical research: creating the building blocks of animal models. Animal Biotechnology. 16:183-190.

Schwann, T. 1836. Ueber das wesen des verdauungsprocesses. Müllers Arch. Anat. Physiol. 90-138.

Schwann, T. and M.J. Schleiden. 1847. Microscopical Researches Into the Accordance in the Structure and Growth of Animals and Plants. London: The Sydenham Society.

Seaman, J. and T.J. Fangman. 2001. Biosecurity for today's swine operation. University of Missouri Cooperative Extension Service. G2340.

Sell, R. 1993. Llama. North Dakota State University Extension Service. Alternative Agriculture Series, Number 12.

Stickney, R.R. 2005. Aquaculture: an introductory text. Wallingford:CABI Publishing.

Stoka, G., J.F. Smith, J.R. Dunham, T. Van Anne. 1997. Lameness in dairy cattle. Kansas State University Agricultural Experiment Station and Cooperative Extension Service. MF-2070.

Swenson, M.J. (Ed.). 1977. Duke's physiology of domestic animals. Ithaca: Cornell University Press.

Thiruvenkadan, A.K., N. Kandasamy, and S. Panneerselvam. 2008. Coat color inheritance in horses. Livest. Sci. 117:109-129.

Thomas, D. 1996. Dairy Sheep Basics for Beginners. In: Proceedings of the Great Lakes Dairy Sheep Symposium. Cornell University, Ithaca, NY. 0–77. Retrived from www.ansci.wisc.edu/Extension-New%20copy/sheep/Publications_and_Proceedings/Pdf/Dairy/Management/Daily%20sheep%20basics%20for%20beginners.pdf

Trut, L., I. Oskina, and A. Kharlamova. 2009. Animal evolution during domestication: the domesticated fox as a model. BioEssays. 31:349-360.

Tyler, H.D. and M.E. Ensminger. 2004. Dairy science. 4th ed. Upper Saddle River: Pearson Prentice Hall.

Tyndale-Biscoe, C.H. 2001. Australasian marsupials - to cherish and to hold. Reprod. Fertil. Dev. 13:477-485.

United States Department of Agriculture, Agriculture Research Service. 2006. Livestock Behavior Research Unit. Mission statement. Retrieved from http://www.ars.usda.gov/main/site_main.htm?modecode=36-02-20-00.

United States Department of Agriculture, Animal Plant Health and Inspection Services. 2009. Dairy 2007. Part IV: Reference of dairy cattle health and management practices in the United States. N494.0209.

United States Department of Agriculture, Animal Plant Health and Inspection Services. 2006. The goat industry: structure, concentration, demand and growth. Retrieved from http://www.aphis.usda.gov/vs/ceah/cei/bi/emergingmarketcondition_files/goatreport090805.pdf.

United States Department of Agriculture, Animal Plant Health and Inspection Services. Wildlife Services. 1997. Bird Predation and Its Control at Aquaculture Facilities in the Northeastern United States. APHIS 11-55-009.

United States Department of Agriculture, Census of Agriculture. Census of Aquaculture. 2005. Retrieved from http://www.agcensus.usda.gov/Publications/2002/Aquaculture/index.asp.

United States Department of Agriculture, Economic Research Service. Data sets; Aquaculture data. 2009. Retrieved from http://www.ers.usda.gov/Browse/view.aspx?subject=AnimalProducts.

United States Department of Agriculture, Economic Research Service. Food availability (per capita) data system. 2009. Retrieved from http://www.ers.usda.gov/Data/FoodConsumption/.

United States Department of Agriculture, Economic Research Service. Blayney, D.P. 2002. The changing landscape of US Milk production. SBN978.

United States Department of Agriculture, Economic Research Service. Dimitir, C. and C. Greene. 2002. Recent growth patterns in the US organic foods market. AIB777.

United States Department of Agriculture, Economic Research Service. Haley, M.M. 2009. Livestock, Dairy, and Poultry Outlook. LDP-M-145.

United States Department of Agriculture, Economic Research Service. Miller, J.J. and D.P. Blayney. 2006. Dairy Backgrounder. LDP-M-145-01.

United States Department of Agriculture, Forest Service. Bisson, P.A. 2006. Assessment of the risk of invasion of national forest streams in the Pacific Northwest by farmed Atlantic salmon. PNW-GTR-697.

United States Department of Agriculture, National Agricultural Library. Adams, B. and J. Larson. 2007. Legislative history of the animal welfare act. AWIC Resource Series No. 41.

United States Department of Agriculture, National Agricultural Statistics Service. Quick Stats: Agricultural Statistics Database. 2009. Retrieved from http://www.nass.usda.gov/QuickStats/indexbysubject.jsp?Pass_group=Livestock+%26+Animals.

United States Department of Agriculture, Natural Resources Conservation Service. Aschmann S. and J. Cropper. 2007. Profitable grazing-based dairy systems. Range and Pasture Tech. Note. 1.

Vilá, C., J.A. Leonard, A. Götherström, S. Marklund, K. Sandberg, K. Lidén, R. Wayned, and H. Ellegren. 2001. Widespread origins of domestic horse lineages. Science. 291:474-477.

Vodičřka, P., K. Smetana, B. Dvo_ánková, T. Emerick, Y.Z. Xu, J. Ourednik, V. Ourednik, and J. Motlík. 2005. The miniature pig as an animal model in biomedical research. Ann. N.Y. Acad. Sci. 1049:161-171.

Wallace, R.K. 2001. Cultivating the eastern oyster *Crassostrea virginica.* Southern Regional Aquaculture Center. SRAC432.

Ward, C. 1997. Vertical integration comparison: beef, pork, and poultry. Oklahoma Cooperative Extension Service. WF552.

Watson, J.D., M. Gilman, J. Witkowski, and M. Zoller. 1992. Recombinant DNA. 2nd ed. New York: W.H. Freeman and Company.

Wayne, R.K. and E.A. Ostrander. 2007. Lessons learned from the dog genome. Trends in Genetics. 23:557-567.

Webster, J. 2005. Animal welfare: limping towards eden. Oxford: Blackwell Publishing.

White, K., B. O'Neill, and Z. Tzankova. 2004. At a crossroads: will aquaculture fulfill the promise of the blue revolution? Report for the SeaWeb Aquaculture Clearinghouse.

Wilmut, I., L. Young, P. DeSousa, and T. King. 2000. New opportunities in animal breeding and production: an introductory remark. An. Repro. Sci. 60-61:5-14.

Wilson, E.B. 1925. The cell. New York: Macmillan.

Wilson, E.O. 1999. The Diversity of Life. New York: Norton, W. W. & Company, Inc.

Wilstach, F.J. 1990. A dictionary of similes. 2nd ed. Detroit: Omingraphics, Inc.

Wolff, J.A. and J. Lederberg. 1994. An early history of gene therapy and transfer. Human Gene Therapy. 5: 469-480.

Wood, G. 1937. Wood, hard-bitten. The Art Digest. 18.

World Health Organization. Epidemic and Pandemic Alert and Response. Avian influenza. Retrieved from http://www.who.int/csr/disease/avian_influenza/en/.

Zawistowski, S. 2008. Companion animals in society. Clifton Park: Thomson Delmar Learning.

Glossary

abomasum   The glandular stomach compartment of ruminant animals located prior to the small inestine.

acid-base balance   The body's balance between acidity and alkalinity. It is precisely controlled by biological buffering systems, excretion of compounds through the kidneys, and respiration processes of the lungs.

ad libitum   Having feed available at all times.

alevin   The larval stage of salmon development that follows hatching and precedes the absorption of the yolk sac. Alleles.

allele   One of two or more alternative forms of a gene occupying corresponding sites (loci) on homologous (similar) chromosomes.

allometric   Unequal growth rates of part of an organism relative to the whole organism.

amylase   Enzyme that catalyzes the break-down of starch.

anadromous   Migrating from sea to fresh water to spawn. Characteristic of the reproductive behavior of salmon.

anaerobic   Conditions that lack oxygen.

anestrus   Period of time when a female is not displaying regular estrous cycles.

aneuploidy   Abnormal chromosome number, a chromosome number that is not an exact multiple of the monoploid (single set—haploid).

anion   An ionic species that carries a negative charge.

anthropomorphism   Attributing human thoughts, emotions, and characteristics to animals.

antioxidant   Substances that protect cells against cellular damage caused by free radicals, which are produced during metabolism and may be increased by environmental factors. Free radicals are unstable compounds that lack complete paired electrons and will attempt to stabilize by removing electrons from other molecules, including those within the cell membrane, and will decrease the stability of the molecule from which the electron was obtained.

aquaculture   The farming of aquatic orginisms including fish, mollusks, crustaceans, and plants.

artificial insemination   Means of placing semen in the female reproductive tracts by means other than natural mating.

ataxia   Lack of muscle coordination and movement.

atresia   Degeneration of follicles that do not make it to the mature, or Graafian stage.

autosomes   All chromosomes other than sex chromosomes.

barr body   The inactivated X chromosome in normal females (or Z in male poultry). Inactivation is a random event that occurs early in embryonic development as a result of folding into an inactive chromatin structure.

barrow   A castrated male hog.

binocular vision   The use of both eyes together to maintain visual focus on an object.

biosecurity   Prodcedures designed to minimize disease transmission from outside and inside a production unit.

blastocyst   The structure of early embryogenesis prior to implantation. It consists of an inner and outer cell mass that gives rise to the embryo and placenta, respectively.

blastomere   The cells that result from the cleavage of a fertilized ovum, preceding the formation of the blastocyst.

bloat   Abnormal quantities of gas collecting in the fermentive portion of the digestive tract.

boar   An intact male pig.

bolus   A rounded mass formed during mastication that initiates the swallowing reflex.

bovine somatotropin (BST)   A naturally produced growth hormone in cattle. Artificially produced bovine somatotropin, otherwise known as recombinant bovine somatotropin (rBST) is manufactured from bacteria and approved for use in dairy cattle for increased milk yield.

breeding value   The worth of an individual as a parent.

broiler   A chicken of either sex used for meat purposes.

calorie   The measue of food energy.

candling   Inspection of the inside of an intact egg with a light to detect defects.

carbohydrate   Any of a group of organic compounds that includes sugars, starches, celluloses, and gums and serves as a major energy source in the diet of animals. These compounds are produced by photosynthetic plants and contain only carbon, hydrogen, and oxygen, usually in the ratio 1:2:1.

carnivore   Animals that subsist on flesh/meat.

caruncle   Outgrowth of the endometrium that serves as the maternal contribution to the placenta in bovines.

catalysis   The process by which enzymes increase the rate of a reaction without being consumed in the process.

cation   An ionic species that carries a positive charge.

caudal   At or near the posterior end or tail of the body.

cellulose   Carbohydrate composed of glucose molecules that forms the support structure of plants.

chromatin   The folded complex of nucleic acids and primarily histone proteins within cells.

chromosome   Deoxyribonucleic acid (DNA) containing structures within cells.

chyme   Mixture of food, saliva, and gastric secretions as it is ready to leave the stomach.

circadian rhythm   The daily rhythmic cycle of activity that occurs within a 24 hour window.

cis   On the same side.

cloning   The process of producing a genetic copy of a gene, DNA segment, embryo, or animal.

coagulation   To thicken or form a clot as in the process of blood coagulation.

collagen   Fibrous extracellular proteins that form the connective tissues of the skin, bone, cartilage, tendons, and teeth.

colostrum   Specialized milk produced in the initial days after parturition. Colostrum is higher in vitamins, mineral, and protein compared with normal milk and generally carries antibodies depending on the species.

conception   The point of time the ovum is fertilized by sperm.

coprophagy   The act of eating feces.

copulation   The act in which the male reproductive organ enters the females reproductive organ.

corpus luteum   Progesterone secreting structure of the ovary developed after the release of the follicle during ovulation.

cotyledon   The fetal contribution to the placenta of bovines.

cranial   Toward the head.

cria   The newborn offspring of llamas and alpacas.

cribbing   A stereotypical behavior observed in stabled horses that involves grasping an object with the incisors, pulling against the object, and sucking in air.

cross-breeding   Mating of genetically diverse breeds within a species.

cryptorchid   Failure of one or both testes to descend into the scrotum.

Cull   Removal of inferior or undesirable animals from the group.

deglutination   The act of swallowing.

denature   To disrupt the structure of a native (protein) causing it to lose its ability to perform its required function.

dentition   Teeth, including the type, number, and positioning.

deoxyribonucleic acid (DNA)   The primary component of chromosomes that represents the blue-print of life and is the material of genetic inheritance.

dermatitis   Inflammation of the skin.

digestion   The physical, chemical, and enzymatic means the body uses to prepare a feedstuff for absorption.

diploid   Having two sets of chromosomes.

discoidal   Having a flat, disk-shape. In primates, refers to the type of placentation whereby maternal and fetal attachments are restricted to a circular plate.

diurnal   Active by day.

dominant   When one member of an allele pair is expressed to the exclusion of the other.

dorsal   Toward or near the back or upper surface of an animal.

double helix   The spiral arrangement of complementary strands of DNA

dry matter   Everything in a feed excluding water.

dystocia   Abnormal or difficult labor

ectoderm   The outer of the three primary germ layers of the embryo that will develop into skin, nervous tissue, and sensory tissues.

embryo transfer   Collecting embryos from a female and transferring to a surrogate for gestation.

emulsify   To form an emulsion or suspension of lipid droplets in a aqueous phase.

Endocrine   Cellular signaling by which an extracellular signaling molecule is released and distributed through the body by blood to act on a remote target.

endoderm   The inner of the three primary germ layers of the embryo that will develop into gastrointestinal and reproductive tracts, and endocrine organs.

endogenous   Pertaining to inside or within an organism or system.

enzymes   Proteins capable of catalyzing reactions.

epididymis   Duct connecting testis with the vas deferens. Responsible for sperm storage, transport, and maturation.

epistasis   Interaction of genes at different loci. Expression of genes at one loci depends on alleles present at another.

epithelium   Tissue that covers the external and lines the internal surface of the body and its organs.

eructation   The act of belching that is common amongst ruminant animals.

estrogen   Any of a group of steroid hormones that regulate the growth, development, and function of the female reproductive tract. The major active estrogen compound in females is estradiol.

estrous cycle   Time from one period of sexual receptivity in the female to the next.

estrus   Period when a female is receptive to mating.

ethogram   A descriptive catalog of the behaviors displayed by a species.

ethology   Study of animals in their natural or most common environment.

etiology   Study of factors that cause disease.

exocrine   Pertaining to the release of a secretion into a duct.

exogenous   Originating from outside of the organism or system.

expression   Manifestation of characteristics that is specified by a gene.

farrow   Act of giving birth in swine.

feed   Food given to animals, which contain nutrients and meet the demands of living organisms.

feedback   Regulatory circuits that may have either a positive or negative effect on biological systems by influencing either enzyme action or hormone release.

felt(felting)   Fabrics that are made from matted, compressed animal fibers (felting is the act of making felt that is popular among knitters).

feral   Having returned to an untamed state following domestication.

filly   A young female horse.

finishing   The final feeding stage when animals are readied for market.

flight zone   The distance which an animal is caused to flee from an intruder.

fluid mosaic model

follicle-stimulating hormone   FSH. Hormone responsible for growth, development, and maintenance of follicles in females.

food   Substances that are consumed, which contain nutrients and meet the demands of living organisms.

forestomachs   Three digestive compartments of the ruminant preceeding the abomasum (true stomach).

CONTRIBUTORS

Patricia H. Berry, PhD, APRN-BC, CHPN®
Assistant Professor
College of Nursing
University of Utah
Salt Lake City, UT

Cathleen A. Collins, RN, MSN, CHPN®
Assistant Professor
Texas Tech University Health Sciences Center
School of Nursing
Lubbock, TX

Constance Dahlin, RN, APRN, BC-PCM
Palliative Care Nurse Practioner
Massachusetts General Hospital
Palliative Care Service
Boston, MA

Mary Ersek, PhD, RN
Research Scientist
Pain Research Department
Swedish Medical Center—Providence Campus
Seattle, WA

Linda Gorman, RN, MN, APRN, BC, CHPN®,
   OCN
Palliative Care/Hospice Clinical Nurse
   Specialist
Cedars Sinai Medical Center
Los Angeles, CA

Lynda Gruenewald-Schmitz, MSN, RN, CHPN®
Clinical Director
Seasons Hospice and Palliative Care
Milwaukee, WI

Barbara Anderson Head, RN, CHPN®, ACSW
Program Coordinator
University of Louisville
Louisville, KY

Kathy Kalina, RN, BSN, CHPN®
Director of Inpatient Services
Community Hospice of Texas
Fort Worth, TX

Judy Lentz, RN, MSN, NHA
Chief Executive Officer
Hospice and Palliative Nurses Association
Pittsburgh, PA

Jeanne Martinez, RN, MPH, CHPN®
Quality and Education Specialist
Northwestern Memorial Home Health Care
Chicago, IL

Marianne LaPorte Matzo, PhD, APRN, GNP
   BC, FAAN
Professor of Nursing
New Hampshire Community Technical College
Manchester, NJ

Judith A. Paice, PhD, RN, FAAN
Director, Cancer Pain Program
Northwestern University
Feinberg School of Medicine
Division of Hematology-Oncology
Chicago, IL

Beverly Paukstis, RN, MS, CHPN®
Director of Clinical Services
Hospice of Naples, Inc.
Naples, FL

Molly A. Poleto, BSN, CHPN®
Director, Quality and Research Initiatives
Healthcare Association of New York State
Rensselaer, NY

Marty Richards, MSW, LICSW
Social Worker
Private Practice
Port Townsend, WA

Ellen C. Rooney, RNC, BSN
Hospice Nursing and Education Consultant
Fredericksburg, VA

Roger Strong, APRN, BC-PCM
Nurse Practitioner
San Diego Hospice
La Mesa, CA

Lizabeth H. Sumner, RN, BSN
Consultant, Pediatric and Perinatal
Palliative Care
Vista, CA

Dena Jean Sutermaster, RN, MSN, CHPN®
Director of Education/Research
Hospice and Palliative Nurses Association
Pittsburgh, PA

Christy Torkildson, RN, PHN, MSN
Director
George Mark Children's House
San Leandro, CA

Barbara G. Volker, RN, MSN, CHPN®
Consultant/Educator—Hospice and Palliative
  Care
Volker Consulting Service
Fresno, CA

Ashby C. Watson, RN, MS, CS, OCN
Psychosocial Oncology Clinical Nurse
  Specialist
MCV Hospitals & Physicians of the Virginia
  Commonwealth University Health System
Richmond, Virginia

Margery A. Wilson, MSN, FNP, CHPN®,
  APRN, BC-PCM
Palliative Care Nurse Practitioner
Wellmont Health System
Bristol, TN

Sarah A. Wilson, PhD, RN
Associate Professor
Marquette University
Milwaukee, WI

EXPERT REVIEWERS

Deronica Austin, BSN
RN On-Call
Hospice, Inc.
Poughkeepsie, NY

Eileen Bennett, RN, BSN, OCN, CHPN®
Nurse Manager
Wellmont Hospice
Bristol, TN

Sue Boederker, RN, BSN, MSN
ADN Instructor
Gateway Technical College
Burlington, WI

Linda F. Hill, LPN
Hospice of Naples
Naples, FL

Kathleen Lavorgna, LPN
Utilization Review
Hospice of Dayton
Dayton, OH

Katherine Miller, BSN, RN
Director of Patient Services
Hospice, Inc.
Poughkeepsie, NY

Douglas Nee, PharmD, MS
Clinical Specialist/Consultant
Pain Management & Palliative Care
DR-Scripts, Inc.
San Diego, CA

Linda B. Rahilly, RN, C, CHPN®
Community Educator and Case Manager
Albemarle Regional Hospice
Edenton, NC

Carla-Lisa Rovere-Kistner, MSW
Director of Patient Services
Hospice, Inc.
Poughkeepsie, NY

Carol Shenise, MS, RN
Education Specialist
The Community Hospice, Inc.
Rensselaer, NY

Pam Stephenson, BN, MSN, CS, AOCN,
   CHPN®
Clinical Nurse Specialist
Forum Health Cancer Care Centers
Youngstown, OH

Kay Terry, RN, MSN, APRN
Nurse Practitioner
Care Source
Salt Lake City, UT

Tanya Walakovits, CHPLN
Home Care LPN
Capital Hospice
Washington, DC

Lana Walsh, LPN
Hospice of Naples
Naples, FL

Leslie Weichsel, MSN, APRN, BC
Vice President of Patient Services
Hospice, Inc.
Poughkeepsie, NY